SAY WHEN
Everything a woman needs
alcohol and drinking

ROSEMARY KENT grew up in South Africa and
moved to Britain in 1975. She now teaches at the
University of Kent at Canterbury, training counsellors,
nurses and social workers to help people with alcohol
problems. She also counsels problem drinkers herself,
and runs assertiveness courses for women.

Overcoming Common Problems Series

The ABC of Eating
Coping with anorexia, bulimia and
compulsive eating
JOY MELVILLE

An A–Z of Alternative Medicine
BRENT Q. HAFEN AND KATHRYN J.
FRANDSEN

Arthritis
Is your suffering really necessary?
DR WILLIAM FOX

Being the Boss
STEPHEN FITZSIMON

Birth Over Thirty
SHEILA KITZINGER

Body Language
How to read others' thoughts by their gestures
ALLAN PEASE

Calm Down
How to cope with frustration and anger
DR PAUL HAUCK

Comfort for Depression
JANET HORWOOD

Common Childhood Illnesses
DR PATRICIA GILBERT

Complete Public Speaker
GYLES BRANDRETH

Coping with Depression and Elation
DR PATRICK McKEON

Coping with Stress
DR GEORGIA WITKIN-LANOIL

Coping Successfully with Your Child's Asthma
DR PAUL CARSON

**Coping Successfully with Your Child's Skin
Problems**
DR PAUL CARSON

**Coping Successfully with Your Hyperactive
Child**
DR PAUL CARSON

Curing Arthritis Cookbook
MARGARET HILLS

Curing Arthritis – The Drug-free Way
MARGARET HILLS

**Curing Coughs, Colds and Flu – the Drug-free
Way**
MARGARET HILLS

Curing Illness – The Drug-free Way
MARGARET HILLS

Depression
DR PAUL HAUCK

Divorce and Separation
ANGELA WILLANS

The Epilepsy Handbook
SHELAGH McGOVERN

Everything You Need to Know about Adoption
MAGGIE JONES

**Everything You Need to Know about Contact
Lenses**
DR ROBERT YOUNGSON

**Everything You Need to Know about Your
Eyes**
DR ROBERT YOUNGSON

**Everything You Need to Know about the
Pill**
WENDY COOPER AND TOM SMITH

Everything You Need to Know about Shingles
DR ROBERT YOUNGSON

Family First Aid and Emergency Handbook
DR ANDREW STANWAY

Feverfew
A traditional herbal remedy for migraine and
arthritis
DR STEWART JOHNSON

Fight Your Phobia and Win
DAVID LEWIS

Flying Without Fear
TESSA DUCKWORTH AND DAVID
MILLER

Goodbye Backache
DR DAVID IMRIE WITH COLLEEN
DIMSON

Good Publicity Guide
REGINALD PEPLOW

Overcoming Common Problems Series

Overcoming Common Problems Series

SAY WHEN!

*Everything a woman
needs to know about
alcohol and
drinking problems*

Rosemary Kent

SHELDON PRESS
LONDON

First published in Great Britain by
Sheldon Press, SPCK, Marylebone Road, London NW1 4DU

We are grateful to Tavistock Publications for permission to
reprint R. D. Laing's poem 'She has started to drink', from *Knots*.

We would also like to thank ACCEPT Services Ltd for the
diagram on page 50, and Dr Gloria Litman for the 'Relapse
Precipitants Inventory'.

Kent, Rosemary
   Say when!: everything a woman needs to
   know about alcohol and drinking problems.
   1. Women. Alcoholism. Control
   I. Title   II. Series
   362.2'9286'09429

   ISBN 0–85969–579–4

Typeset by Deltatype, Ellesmere Port, Cheshire
Printed in Great Britain by Biddles Ltd, Guildford, Surrey

Contents

How much alcohol in a drink?

In order to look at how much people drink, we refer to UNITS of alcohol. This makes it easier to compare one kind of drink with another.

½ pint = 1 glass = 1 glass = 1 single = ONE UNIT OF
(250 ml) table   sherry   gin or   ALCOHOL
of beer   wine   whisky

DRINK	UNITS
half pint (250 ml) ordinary lager or beer or light cider	1
1 pint (500 ml) ordinary lager or beer or light cider	2
1 pint (500 ml) Guinness or some 'real ales' or strong lagers	3
1 pint (500 ml) strong cider (such as Blackthorn or Strongbow)	4
1 can 'Special' lager	3
1 glass table wine	1
1 glass sparkling wine or strong wine	2
1 pub measure (⅙ gill) spirits (whisky/gin/vodka etc)	1
1 glass sherry or martini or port	1

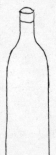

1 bottle ordinary table wine	7–8
1 bottle sparkling or strong wine	10–12
1 litre bottle table wine	10–12
1 bottle sherry, port, vermouth etc	14
1 bottle spirits (whisky, gin, vodka etc)	30

> 1 UNIT OR STANDARD MEASURE
> CONTAINS 8–10 GRAMS OF ALCOHOL

REMEMBER – ONE PINT (500 ml) OF BEER IS
EQUIVALENT IN STRENGTH TO A DOUBLE BRANDY

1

Drinking—just a habit?

Why do we drink? Why do *you* drink? It's not often that we stop to ask questions about our drinking—it's so much part of our way of life, part of our culture, even part of family life. Alcohol is associated with drinking a toast, with celebrations and rituals, good food and companionship—and with drowning our sorrows. We drink because 'it's the done thing' and other people expect it of us. Although we usually only start drinking in our teens, the roots of our drinking habits normally lie embedded within the family. Not just our parents, but neighbours, advertisements and what we read and see on television all gradually influence our expectations of our own and others' drinking.

To understand something about similarities and differences in people's adult drinking patterns, we need to consider the influences that emerge as we grow up, affecting the 'where?', 'what?', and 'why?' of our drinking. We have somehow to learn that alcohol is not simply a Bad Thing (it can make you sick, cause traffic accidents, lead to 'alcoholism'), nor simply a Good Thing (it makes you relaxed, tastes good, is sophisticated), but that there are different ways of reacting to alcohol. We gradually learn to differentiate, for example, between appropriate social drinking, drunkenness, heavy drinking and alcoholism.

We may have early memories about drinking habits and the effects of alcohol on our elders and betters. There may have been whispered rumours about 'Uncle Bill was a terrible old drunk', or a cousin who drank too much at a party and fell down the stairs. Or 'my mother would never travel in the car with my father if he'd had a drink, and there'd be a row', or 'I remember my grandmother always getting very sentimental at Christmas dinner—when she had *two* glasses of sherry.' For some children there are unhappy memories—there may have been a strong association between alcohol and rows or a break-up in the family. These memories, the example set by people close to us, and the messages we receive directly—such as religious ideas about the use of alcohol—will vary from one family to another and one society to another.

Family drinking habits

Janet

Janet grew up in a small town, where her father was a minister. Her

1

parents followed the teachings of the Bible closely, and Janet's upbringing was strict. While Janet's father was more worldly-wise than her mother, both of them viewed drinking alcohol as something dangerous and sinful. On one occasion in Janet's childhood she saw her father drink a glass of rum, as a toast, and she remembered it in every detail. It was Christmas Eve and she was ten or eleven, and her aunt and her new husband had come to spend Christmas with them. It was the first time Janet had met them, as they lived some distance away, and her parents had worried about not going to the wedding. The new uncle seemed immediately at ease in their house, and had barely sat down when he produced a bottle of rum from a bag and said he wanted to 'propose a toast'. Janet remembered her puzzlement over this strange announcement, thinking it very rude to ask for toast in that manner! Her mother seemed more shocked than even Janet would have expected her to be, until she realized that it was the bottle of rum that had caused her mother's dismay. Janet's father opened the bottle of rum and poured a tiny amount into a glass for himself, for Aunt Ruth, and for Uncle Jack. He then coughed, and said he was very happy to welcome Uncle Jack and Aunt Ruth and as it was so special an occasion he would drink a toast with them. It was the only time Janet had seen drink in the house, and she was horrified to see these three adults sipping their drinks in silence, and then Uncle Jack seeming embarrassed and putting the rum away. For many years afterwards Janet thought of that afternoon, and was apprehensive that someone might expect her to take a drink of the terrifying stuff. Her parents did not discuss drinking with her, and she knew that it was a 'taboo' subject.

Pat

Pat grew up with three brothers — she was second eldest. Her mother had been a dressmaker and then when all the children were at school she worked in a department store. Her father ran a small business and was sometimes away during the week, so that Friday evenings were often a sort of family reunion, and weekends were a time for doing things together. They lived in a close where they knew all the neighbours, with a pub at the corner, less than half a mile from the house. Pat's father always called in at the pub on a Sunday, and her mother would sometimes go with him while the dinner was in the oven. All the children had been into the pub on and off during their childhood, as the landlord was a friend, and not particularly strict. Pat remembered times when she had stood next to her father and he had told her to 'run along home now', when she knew it was because some of the men there seemed to be acting stupidly. At home, her brothers were allowed to drink shandy when they were quite young but she was not allowed to have her first sip of wine until she was fifteen. Pat was irritated that there were times when her older and younger brothers would be allowed to drink beer with their father, and she was not offered anything alcoholic to drink. Sometimes she took her cue from her mother who would gently poke fun at the men sitting around with their glasses, discussing the affairs of the world. She occasionally allowed herself a gin and tonic when she was relaxing in the evening, and Pat associated that with her mother being contented—and a little bit daring. When neighbours visited, usually the men would go down to the pub, while she and her mother stayed behind with the women who were visiting. All in all, by the time she left home, she had come to see the pub as a friendly but predominantly male territory, with not much to attract her as a homely teenage girl. There was alcohol in the house, and this she regarded as something for occasional adult celebrations, or with which her parents relaxed.

Trudy

Trudy's memories of childhood were mostly about moving house many times—sometimes being sent away to boarding school then returning each summer holiday to a different home. Her grand-parents, who were Norwegian, had lived with them when she was very young, and her parents and grandparents always had wine with their meals, and whisky or brandy or gin beforehand. They entertained frequently too—there were always parties with quanti-ties of food and alcohol, but often there were arguments which Trudy began to associate with the parties, and then associated the parties with people being drunk. She was an only child, and was expected to behave in an adult way. When she came back from school on holidays in her teens she joined in the drinking and socializing, copying the sophisticated young women who drifted around at her parents' parties. At school she was seen as a rebel, and it was rumoured that she bought gin at weekends and drank it in the school grounds with a few daring friends. At home her parents would remark proudly how mature she was, when she joined them for drinks before dinner. She watched her mother quickly gulping a few glasses of wine in the kitchen before she became the charming hostess at dinners, or when she and her father went out to smart restaurants. Trudy realized how powerful alcohol could be, and also how convenient, as it switched her parents' moods, and ensured that any social occasion went with a swing. It seemed too that

3

drinking was a sort of international passport, for many of her parents' friends travelled widely and there were often visitors from many different parts of the world.

Janet, Pat and Trudy have very different backgrounds, but all have been influenced by their parents' expectations and lifestyle, their neighbourhood and their culture. Attitudes to alcohol are woven into their lives in ways which affect their future drinking patterns and how they feel about their drinking. Families are not the only influence, but some understanding of what was considered acceptable or not acceptable in childhood helps make sense of behaviour in later life.

Learning how to drink

Copying our elders, or doing what others in a group of friends are doing, is a universal way of learning how to behave. This happens whether or not this behaviour is 'right' or 'wrong': it will simply be viewed by the young child as familiar, or 'that's just the way things are'. So in a family or neighbourhood where, for example, people get drunk on Friday nights and become noisy and violent, this may be the pattern that the child recreates in his or her adult life. If a child sees her mother using drink as a way of escaping from unpleasant circumstances, or making it possible for her to stand up for herself, she may come to use alcohol for these reasons too, later in life. Trudy, for example, soon learned that alcohol had all sorts of uses—because her parents showed her. Some women may consciously choose to avoid alcohol, or not drink alcohol in particular ways or for particular reasons, in their late teens and early adulthood, and then find that they return at a later stage to drinking in ways that can be traced back to early patterns in their family—particularly in times of stress.

What about families or environments where drinking occurs without any apparent problems, such as in Pat's home? Drinking alcohol is learned along with other social skills, and is associated with leisure, mealtimes, relaxation and ceremonial occasions, and we learn that there are informal 'rules' about what is 'normal' drinking behaviour. We have to learn to enjoy the taste of alcohol—most children will screw up their faces at their first sip of wine or beer!

In many western countries there are certain times when having a drink is 'normal': before and during midday and evening meals, and during the evening. There are norms about where we drink and who with (for example, in pubs, and at parties; with friends, not with children), and the activities that are going to follow drinking or influence the quantity of time spent drinking—for example, driving a car, getting up in the night to feed a baby, going to work.

In a teetotal environment, like Janet's, children may not have opportunities to learn about the part alcohol can play in *normal* social life. Alcohol may be regarded as evil, or just as something that one can or should do without. This may be part of the families' religious beliefs, or may be because of finance, health reasons, tradition, or other circumstances. Some of these children may grow up to develop erratic or excessive drinking habits, as they have not had the opportunity to imitate adults' use of alcohol, or experiment for themselves. On the other hand they may remain teetotal, or they may develop moderate drinking patterns through mixing with non-teetotal friends after leaving their parents' home.

'Drinking like a lady'

Some of the most important 'messages' we are given about drinking are common to many families and many cultural backgrounds—but are different for boys and for girls. Even in families with a fairly 'liberal' view of teenagers experimenting with alcohol, there is still the idea that it is more shocking for adolescent girls to get drunk than adolescent boys. There may be amusement at boys being 'one of the lads', while on the other hand a girl being drunk is definitely 'not ladylike'. A boy may be encouraged to drink 'like a man'; a girl is expected to be more cautious and moderate in her use of alcohol. Television, magazine and billboard advertisements play a big part in this too—they often present sherry, wine and cocktails as glamorous, sophisticated and even romantic, and thus appropriate for 'feminine' tastes. Men's drinks are associated usually with success in business or sport, and advertising aimed at men is primarily of beer or spirits. In many western societies this theme of what sort of drinking is acceptable for males and females occurs in traditional customs: a bridegroom is expected to drink large quantities on the eve of his wedding (or even on his wedding day!), whereas a drunken bride would be regarded with considerable alarm!

A man's frequent and regular drinking is seen as acceptable if it fits into a traditional pattern of male work and relaxation—for instance, he may spend his lunch hours in a pub and call in there two or three times a week on his way home from work. A woman who spent this amount of time in a drinking environment would probably be gossiped about. And if she drank this often on her own, the disapproval would be even greater.

In addition to types of drinks, and circumstances appropriate for drinking, we learn that larger quantities and certain effects are more acceptable in men than women. The young man is likely to feel more pressurized by his friends into drinking a third or a fourth pint, than a woman. It would also be quite usual for a young woman to say 'oh, no if I have more than two glasses, I'll get terribly giggly' than for a man to admit this sort of reaction to alcohol! Thus, drinking heavily, or getting drunk often, is discouraged by our families and society as a whole. It can be doubly shameful for a woman who develops drinking habits out of step with those around her—she is assumed to have given up on her femininity as well as being unable to control her drinking.

Growing up

Through our childhood and teenage years, we gradually absorb ideas about what alcohol can do, and something about what sort of drinking is appropriate to our gender, age and culture. A new set of influences will begin to play their part when we move away from the supervision of parents, and as young adults our drinking patterns will begin to reflect the circle of friends we have and lifestyle we move into. As we leave school or start a job or further education, we meet different groups of people and may move away from home. Interests change—we may become more (or less) concerned about keeping fit, a healthy diet, or about experimenting with food, smoking or drinking. Travel or study or a new boyfriend or girlfriend can bring about a shift in what we drink, how much, and in what circumstances. Sometimes in our teens and twenties our drinking may be rather chaotic, with heavy drinking at parties or in response to emotional ups and downs. The very fact of being 'in transition' may lead us to drink more for a period of time as a way of coping with change. For many women, the late teens and early twenties is a time of being adventurous, and drinking may be part of asserting freedom from parents. It is also common for people to discover for themselves during this time just how powerful and convenient alcohol can be as a relaxant, a pacifier, a 'pick-me-up' or confidence-booster. Both individual and group pressures now provide reasons for drinking, and these are added to the earlier, family-based influences on drinking habits.

What part has alcohol played in your life?

Copy Pat's idea of drawing a graph to show how your drinking habits has changed over the years. Note the ages or phases in your life when your drinking habits shifted, and link them to events or aspects of your family life, social life, health, work, interests or friendships which influenced those habits.

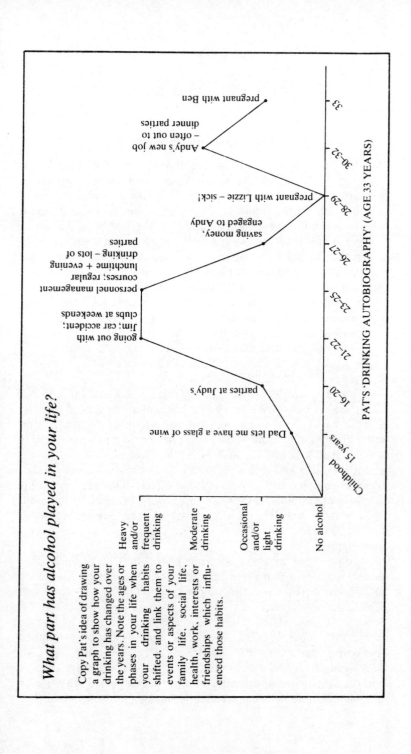

PAT'S 'DRINKING AUTOBIOGRAPHY' (AGE 33 YEARS)

2

Knowing when you are 'at risk'

What does alcohol do?

Alcohol changes how people feel, and how they behave, because it is a drug. It *directly* affects our thinking, balance and coordination because of its chemical properties; it slows down or reduces some of the functions of the brain. It also affects us *indirectly* (a) because when our mood changes and we feel less inhibited, we are likely to behave in a more relaxed way; and (b) because we gradually learn to *expect* that drinking is going to result in certain feelings and actions; for example, 'If I have a few glasses of wine at a party, I won't feel so shy, and I'll be able to appear more sociable'.

So, people drink for many understandable and specific purposes: they are aware of the 'usefulness' of alcohol. Those who produce and market alcoholic beverages are obviously interested in high-lighting the good and useful side of drinking, and underplaying those aspects which are harmful. In this book we will try to look at *both* sides of what alcohol can do to us.

It is a drug which is socially acceptable, in moderation, and it is cheap and effective. We know that it has many beneficial aspects, and we *believe* that it has many more; for instance, there is no scientific reason to drink whisky if one has a cold, but we stubbornly believe that it helps! As well as its chemical effects, and beliefs about how it is going to affect individuals physically and psycho-logically, alcohol has powerful social effects. Drinking alcohol is symbolic at many social events, conjuring up a sense of hospitality, 'togetherness' or celebration. It forms part of many religious rituals and ceremonies, and is used to signify goodwill, or seal formal agreements.

Alcohol is not 'all good' for some people and 'all bad' for other people in the way that some advertising and the images that we see on television, in films and in books portray it. Everyone will sometimes experience the costs of alcohol and sometimes its benefits. Drink-related problems (costs) can happen to anyone who drinks, whether it is an occasional hangover or being stopped and losing one's licence when driving a car 'over the limit', or developing liver disease. Sometimes these problems are chronic and keep recurring, or there may be one specific period in a person's life when problems occur frequently, and then a time when they disappear. Drinking problems can appear and disappear, but for some people their problems can increase and become harder to resolve over a period of years. Health problems in particular may remain hidden for many years. Drinking is a risky business, and it is not always easy to predict its effects!

The properties of alcohol

Alcohol is a drug with the capacity to alter mood and behaviour. At first, the drinker's sense of inhibition is reduced, so that in company she feels excited and talkative, or on her own, she may feel depressed or mildly anaesthetized. With more drink, there is slurring of speech, unsteadiness, drowsiness, and reduced ability to concentrate and remember things. More drinking leads to the person being less able to relate to her environment appropriately, sometimes losing her inhibitions and becoming aggressive, paranoid, self-pitying, or totally 'in a world of her own'. At very high levels of concentration of alcohol in the blood, the entire functioning of the body is depressed, the drinker becomes drowsy, and reflexes, blood pressure, and body temperature all drop. Death can result from taking very large quantities of alcohol, either through the depressant effect it has on that part of the brain which controls breathing, or (at an earlier stage of intoxication) from inhaling vomit.

Alcohol is a 'toxin'—a poison. High concentrations of alcohol can interfere with the circulation of the blood and with the absorption of certain nutrients in our food, and can cause irritation or inflammation of body tissues. Very large quantities of alcohol taken over a short period of time can cause death through alcoholic poisoning. It is important to remember that the effects of alcohol on the body (both as drug and as toxin) are not all-or-nothing; small amounts can lead to mild intoxication, and can cause minor problems, larger amounts lead to more intoxication and may cause greater physical harm. Related to this, and equally important, is that alcohol has immediate, short-term effects, and also long-term or chronic effects. Long-term effects include muscle damage, vitamin deficiencies, peripheral nerve damage, the likelihood of strokes occurring, memory and perception difficulties, general 'dementing', psychiatric disorders, liver damage, and various types of cancer. When it comes to long-term effects, a 40-year-old woman who has had two or three drinks a week for the past 20 years, is unlikely to experience long-term physical harms, whereas someone who has regularly had

9

four or five drinks every day for 20 years is far more likely to develop one or more physical problems.

Alcohol is also a food, which is high in calories and low on nutrition. Drinking too much can certainly make you fat, for example, by drinking five pints (2.8 litres) of beer in the course of a day, you are taking in about half of the average woman's daily calorie requirements. Very heavy drinkers can in fact suffer from malnutrition, through substituting alcohol for food, and through the toxic effects of alcohol making it difficult for the body to process vitamins. Finally, alcohol is a drug which can produce 'dependence', in other words it can be a *habit-forming drug*. This is discussed in more detail later.

So to summarize so far:

(1) Alcohol has good effects and bad effects.
(2) The damaging effects of drinking alcohol can be mild, moderate or serious.
(3) There are short-term consequences of drinking, and there are effects from an accumulation of heavy drinking over a period of weeks, months or years, that is, long-term consequences.
(4) Drinking habits can lead to 'dependence' on alcohol which may be mild, moderate or severe.

It follows from this that of the many questions that may be asked about 'safe', 'risky', or 'harmful' drinking, not many can be answered with absolute certainty—even by so-called experts—because very often the answer may be 'it depends on the individual'. However, we need to discuss some of the more common worries that women may have about their drinking.

Common concerns about heavy drinking

First, some women worry most about the bad physical consequences alcohol could be having on them such as becoming overweight, or their memory being affected, or a deterioration of their general health. Second, some are worried about the social consequences of their drinking, for instance the effect on their families, or on their ability to hold down a particular job. Third, for some women it is their reasons for drinking about which they feel uneasy. Fourth, some women will want to know whether they are dependent on alcohol. Finally the big question that some women will have in their minds, or will ask aloud, is 'how do I know whether I am an alcoholic?'.

Many of these questions are of course linked to one another, but it may be helpful to try to separate out some of the issues. Many people who are currently drinking moderately or heavily may already be experiencing some physical or other damaging consequences, but they may not be aware of them, or they may not have thought of drinking as being the cause. Some readers of this book may recognize that there is the potential for problems to arise with their drinking in the future. This book aims to reduce the likelihood of your experiencing harm because of your drinking in the future, and to help you reduce existing harm if you already have some problems as a result of your present drinking patterns.

As has been stated, the more you drink the greater the likelihood of experiencing one or more of a range of physical harms. If you cut down your drinking, these risks will be reduced. Also there are certain times in a woman's life when she is less resilient and therefore more vulnerable to the toxic or drug effects of alcohol. These are when pregnant, when taking prescribed medication or illicit drugs, just prior to menstruation, during ovulation, and in later years. A woman who is thin or slight in stature, is likely to experience intoxication and possibly alcohol-related harms, through drinking less, or less often, than someone with a bigger build. Also someone who is young (in their teens) or generally unused to drinking alcohol will find it harder to cope with alcohol in the body than someone who is older or who has had more years to get used to alcohol, that is, to develop 'tolerance'.

Another problem about defining 'safe limits' for the population in general is that many books, research articles, and information pamphlets written prior to 1980 or 1981 paid little attention to the effects of alcohol *on women* specifically. Because in the past drinking has been defined as primarily a male pastime, and excessive or dependent drinking as a male problem, the precise effects of alcohol on women has not been given much attention. Even now research is still very limited, and most of the guidelines given to women can only be approximate, and based on small amounts of evidence. Recently there have been attempts to identify what the generally agreed safe limits of drinking are for women, and to specify the 'danger zone'—in which problems, particularly liver problems, have been shown to be more likely in statistical terms. So, *bearing in mind that there are many special cases and individual differences*, a 'sensible limits chart' is given on the next page.

11

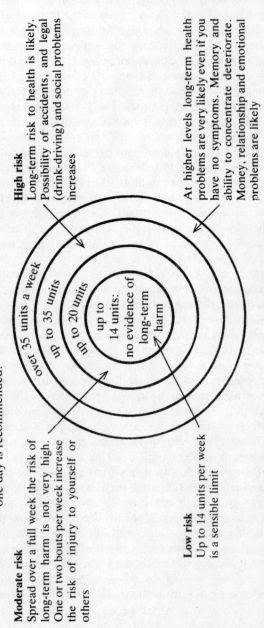

Sensible limits chart

For most healthy women there is no evidence of long-term harm for an average weekly consumption of under 14 units. A limit of 5 units in any one day is recommended.

High risk
Long-term risk to health is likely. Possibility of accidents, and legal (drink-driving) and social problems increases

At higher levels long-term health problems are very likely even if you have no symptoms. Memory and ability to concentrate deteriorate. Money, relationship and emotional problems are likely

over 35 units a week

up to 35 units

up to 20 units

up to 14 units:
no evidence of long-term harm

Moderate risk
Spread over a full week the risk of long-term harm is not very high. One or two bouts per week increase the risk of injury to yourself or others

Low risk
Up to 14 units per week is a sensible limit

'At risk' families

People who have a parent or grandparent who has been dependent on alcohol are statistically more likely to develop alcohol dependence themselves. This may be due to genetic factors, or to the parents' influence on children as they are growing up, or a combination of these. There is also recent evidence that genetic factors may contribute to a higher risk of developing physical problems related to drinking. It appears that some women are more vulnerable than others to developing alcoholic liver cirrhosis, and that this could be an inherited vulnerability. More research is needed to try to unravel the role of genetic factors, the pattern of relationships within families, and the influence of the example set by mothers and fathers to their children, before we can really understand what makes it more or less likely that a woman will develop alcohol problems.

What does being dependent on alcohol mean?

In the same way that there is some general agreement about what levels of drinking are likely to be damaging, there are also certain *reasons* for drinking and ways of behaving which indicate that someone may be 'at risk' of their drinking becoming out of hand. One of the most common warning signs is when alcohol is more and more often used as a way of avoiding feeling bad, particularly if drinking is seen as the *only* way of coping. Another factor in identifying 'at risk' drinking, linked to the idea of dependence on alcohol, is tolerance. This happens as drinkers become more used to drinking larger quantities in order to obtain the same effects that they used to get after just a few drinks. So for example, Trudy (who we met in the first chapter) might find that as a seventeen-year-old she became uninhibited and extrovert when she had drunk only two glasses of gin. By the time she is 27 two gins barely have any effect on her, and if she wants to be lively and sociable she would have to have four or five glasses of gin before going out to a party. Tolerance tends only to occur among people who drink fairly regularly, as the body adapts to processing alcohol more quickly and adjusting the effect it has on the brain, to cope with increased quantities. People who are highly tolerant to alcohol often do not appear to be drunk, and it is often said of such people that they can 'really hold their booze' or 'drink other people under the table'. While this is sometimes seen as a quality to be admired, it does not mean that the long-term effects of alcohol are less damaging. People's natural

13

controls over how much can safely be drunk at any time no longer operate. Harm to the brain and other organs of the body can increase without the drinker realizing it. More money and more energy is spent to try and obtain a heightened effect, so the tolerant drinker becomes out of step with moderate drinkers. For some people, this process can go so far that it is more 'normal' to be topped up with alcohol than not, and the body needs alcohol to function more smoothly. When the concentration of alcohol in the body begins to drop on any given occasion, drinkers tolerant to alcohol begin to feel uncomfortable.

Withdrawal symptoms

Some regular heavy drinkers are likely to experience physical and psychological discomfort a few hours after their last drink, and these we call 'withdrawal symptoms'. The main symptoms are shakiness, nausea, sweating or feeling clammy, edginess, agitation and general mood disturbance, and in extreme circumstances hallucinations and fits.

Drinking to relieve the discomfort of mild, moderate or severe withdrawal symptoms, or drinking to prevent withdrawal symptoms from starting, is one of the more worrying reasons for drinking. As has been mentioned before, this has more to do with the drinker trying to avoid feeling bad, than to do with the more common and socially acceptable reasons for drinking, such as because of the taste, or to relax in social situations, or to celebrate an occasion. Many would say that experiencing withdrawal symptoms is the main sign of 'dependence' on alcohol. The physical aspects that are described above are the most obvious examples of the discomfort that indicates someone may be dependent on alcohol. But while avoiding these physical withdrawal symptoms by drinking alcohol is a clear indication of dependence, regularly relying on alcohol to keep at bay negative feelings such as anxiety or unhappiness, may also be regarded as 'dependent' drinking.

What is *dependence?*

Let us look further at the notion of dependence. Listed below are some behaviour patterns that can be regular and daily features of life. For many people their absence will lead to discomfort. They may be pleasurable or beneficial in the short term, or cause harm in excess or when they take priority over other things.

Smoking
Watching television

14

Drinking tea/coffee
Taking tranquillizers
Gambling
Eating chocolate, sweets or biscuits

Now this may sound as if we are just talking about good and bad habits, and in many ways drinking can be 'just a habit', it is only when we try to give up a habit that we may get an inkling of how dependent we are on it—and perhaps even in danger of losing control over it. People experience varying degrees of difficulty if they try to give up any of the things listed above. Some people would have a fairly rough time giving up, but would manage, either by themselves or with outside help. Others would simply make a decision one day to cease indulging in something, and that would be the end of it. Other people would go through phases of being able to take it or leave it, depending on what is happening in the rest of their lives. Some people may experience many of the unpleasant symptoms described above as withdrawal symptoms when trying to do without.

The question of how dependent you or I are on alcohol is very much about the extent that we feel we can do without it. The 'at risk' aspect becomes increasingly serious when depending on drinking overrides being able to recognize or to act on the fact that it is causing harm. It is sensible to put our dependence upon alcohol to the test. Some people may find that it is best to have a few alcohol-free days each week or alcohol-free weeks every few months, or some people may choose to limit their intake to specified small amounts on certain occasions. For other people the only sure way of ensuring that they maintain a 'non-dependence' on alcohol is to not drink at all, and this is what many people who define themselves as 'alcoholics' choose to do.

The term 'alcoholic' is a shorthand term for people who are both severely dependent on alcohol and experience harmful consequences from their drinking, and whose consumption is regular and excessive. Thus only a proportion of people who are severely dependent on drinking, or have alcohol-related difficulties, fit neatly into this category. Because the words 'alcoholic' and 'alcoholism' are given very different definitions by different people, some people will avoid using the terms, particularly if they think that they make problem drinkers feel stigmatized. For other people this is not the case, and they find that it is a secure and straightforward way of describing a certain type of drinker and his/her condition. Some drinkers will be relieved and encouraged to

15

find that their drinking habits are not unique—they are part of a pattern of behaviours and problems called 'alcoholism'. Finding that others experience what they experience, makes the term 'alcoholic' helpful in relation to themselves. Occasionally some drinkers use these labels to avoid examining their own drinking patterns. Thus, 'an alcoholic can't ever stop drinking. I do sometimes stop, for days at a time even—so I can't be an alcoholic and I don't know why everyone's making such a fuss' is a way of reasoning that can be self-destructive.

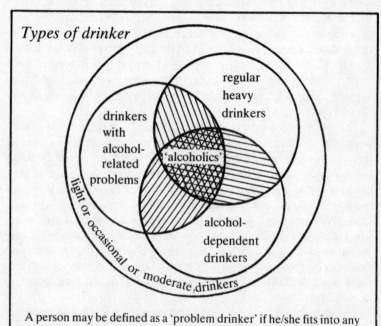

Types of drinker

regular heavy drinkers

drinkers with alcohol-related problems

'alcoholics'

alcohol-dependent drinkers

light or occasional or moderate drinkers

A person may be defined as a 'problem drinker' if he/she fits into any one of the three smaller circles. More commonly, he/she has characteristics of people in two of the three smaller circles. Those who have characteristics of people in all three of the smaller circles are often referred to as 'alcoholics'. People may move in and out of different circles at different times.

3

Alcohol—the socially acceptable drug?

What are the positive things that we believe about alcohol? Why is it that in spite of the harm that it can do, many women drink more than just occasionally? Or indeed drink heavily? There are in addition to our families, many powerful political, economic, social and psychological pressures that influence every woman who drinks—some influence us subtly and gradually, others in a direct and obvious way.

Availability and advertising

Alcohol is easy to obtain, and surveys show that availability and price have a strong effect on people's drinking habits. When the price of alcohol rises, consumption decreases, and the more prosperous a country becomes overall, the more the population in that country will drink. Alcohol has become cheaper since the 1950s; for instance in 1950 the price of a loaf of bread was roughly equivalent to the price it was in 1980 in real terms—that is, it took the average manual worker about nine minutes to earn the amount of money needed to buy a loaf of bread. It took about ten and a half hours to earn the price of a bottle of whisky in 1950, but in 1980 it only took about two hours. Stan Shaw writing a chapter called 'The causes of increasing drinking problems amongst women' in a book entitled *Women and Alcohol* (see Appendix 2), pointed out that in the 1960s a change in the law gave women a more 'direct route' to alcohol: off-licences were allowed to open during normal shopping hours, and supermarkets and many food shops began to have sections selling drink. By 1977 a half of Britain's supermarkets had licences to sell alcohol. Recently, figures show that women are more important than men for bulk purchases from licensed stores.

Alongside this, women's earning and therefore spending power is increasing, and it is more acceptable for women to buy drinks for themselves in pubs, to frequent wine bars, and also to go into some of the heavy drinking occupations that were previously dominated by men, such as journalism and commerce. Women are more obviously part of the drinking culture of many western countries than they were 25 years ago.

The drinks industry and alcohol advertisers are cashing in on these changes. Many millions are spent each year trying to persuade women to drink more—particularly wines and spirits. In spite of a code of conduct which states that advertising should not emphasize the unproven drug effects of alcohol (for example, an advertisement should not imply that brandy makes you more sexually attractive), much of it is geared to getting us to associate certain drinks with success, sophistication and seduction.

Increases in consumption

Since the 1950s, figures have shown very clearly the overall quantity of drinking in Britain is increasing. Between 1950 and 1980 alcohol consumption per head of population more or less doubled—for women this happened more quickly, mainly during the 1970s. The most popular 'womens' drinks' are wine and spirits such as vodka, gin and white rum, where there have been dramatic increases in sales. By 1978 it became evident that more women were drinking wine than men, and women more often bought sherry than men. Wine consumption virtually doubled from 1960 to 1969, then nearly doubled again between 1969 and 1974.

Increasing consumption brings increasing problems. A recent report (1986) by The Royal College of Psychiatrists summarizes some of the evidence for the United Kingdom's experience of alcohol-related problems in general. Every aspect appears to have increased over the last 20 years or so: death from cirrhosis, hospital admissions for alcoholism, drunkenness arrests, and drink/driving arrests. There are particularly worrying statistics which apply to specific groups of people. Taken as a social grouping, the alcohol problems of women as a whole are accelerating—the number of women diagnosed as alcoholic in hospitals trebled between 1964 and 1975; female convictions for drinking and driving used to be 1 per cent of all convictions, but in 1977 were 3 per cent; and the number of deaths from liver cirrhosis has increased from 651 women in 1970 to 915 in 1975. Convictions for drunkenness have increased for all women in all age groups under 60 from 1970 to 1977, but they increased four-fold amongst eighteen to 21-year-olds and three-fold amongst 22–30-year-olds. It appears that the heaviest women drinkers anyway are most likely to be under 25 and unmarried. It is not clear whether being in paid employment influences the quantities women drink, but certain types of jobs may increase pressure to drink more. For example, traditionally heavy drinking occupations are journalism, other media positions, marketing, representative work, advertising, and working in pubs,

18

clubs, restaurants, and hotels. Women are exposed to alcohol more in these jobs, their colleagues might well have heavier drinking habits, and in some of these jobs there might be high stress and emotional pressures.

Reasons for drinking

There are many straightforward, socially acceptable reasons for drinking: the taste, or to quench our thirst. A cool glass of lager on a hot day . . . an after-dinner mint liqueur . . . a good vintage of a fine French wine. Knowing when to 'say when!' is not so difficult when we drink because of these obvious physical sensations. Regulating the amount and frequency of our drinking happens without conscious effort.

But there are other, psychological factors, which vary from one individual to another, that may be harder to understand and to overcome if we want to reduce or stop drinking. Sometimes individual psychological factors overlap with physical factors, such as drinking to relieve pain or tiredness, and sometimes social and psychological pressures overlap too.

In the first chapter, Janet, Pat and Trudy showed examples of what drinking alcohol meant in their particular families. Bearing in mind that the reasons why people start drinking in the first place are not necessarily the same as the reasons why they increase or carry on their drinking, or why their drinking causes them social or psychological problems, it may be useful to look at how Janet, Pat and Trudy drank in their teens and twenties.

Janet

Janet's reasons for not drinking at first were related to the expectations of her family, and the social circles in which she moved when she lived at home. She was frightened of upsetting her mother and being regarded as 'sinful' if she went against what she had been taught. After leaving school Janet stayed at home and worked as a telephonist in a local firm, but when she was 23 she decided to train as a nurse, and moved to a town 20 miles away from her parents' home. At first she felt a complete misfit—she was older than the other student nurses, she was black and most of them were white, she didn't drink and they drank a lot. She felt awkward and lonely and after a few months she gave in to the coaxing and teasing and went out with them to the hospital social club. They persuaded her to have a glass of beer. She didn't enjoy the taste, but with the applause and cheers of others around the bar, she found herself gulping down a second glass. Later in the evening she felt sick and dizzy and angry with herself and the other student nurses, and guilty and worried. And yet she also felt that something important had changed, and that she was an accepted member of the group. From then on, throughout her student nurse training, the more she drank, the more her friends made her the centre of attention, encouraging her to 'stop worrying and start living!'. At parties she drank more than anyone else—she wanted to show she could do it—and anyway she would get worried and anxious and think about her family if she stopped after just one or two drinks.

Pat

Pat started drinking gradually and occasionally in her teens. She went to college at eighteen and lived in a house with four other women—all of them were constantly broke, and if they had spare cash they would buy records or tapes. Music was their passion and their drug, so they seldom drank alcohol. At parties or music concerts Pat would sometimes have beer or wine but it had little effect on her and there seemed to be little attraction in getting drunk. She did occasionally go to raucous drunken parties at her friend Judy's house but on the whole her drinking stayed fairly light until she left college and was going out with Jim. Around that time she was involved in a car crash and for months afterwards she had constant backaches which drained her energy and left her depressed. She discovered that drinking vodka or brandy was an effective temporary painkiller, and enabled her to keep up with Jim's energy and high spirits. And he often knew the owner of the club, or chatted up the barman, or had a supply of brandy from some questionable source—so Pat never had to worry about the expense. Later, she trained as a personnel manager and found that she quickly slipped into a pattern of heavy social drinking. Alcohol seemed to be the focus of her social life: going out to pubs every day, parties, and all-night jazz clubs.

Trudy

In Trudy's life there always seemed to be plenty of reasons for drinking: because her parents did, because she liked being a rebel at school, because she was expected to be sophisticated, because it made parties go with a swing, because it made her able to forget her parents' rows. When she was seventeen, her parents divorced and Trudy felt abandoned and desperate. She went out with many different men, flirted outrageously and distracted herself with new boyfriends at parties and plenty of booze. Things became more chaotic as she used other drugs as well as alcohol – she took amphetamines and alcohol to give her a lift, tranquillizers to bring her down, and large quantities of sleeping tablets when she could not sleep. The worst time was each month just before her period, when she always drank more. She lost 2 stone (12½ kg) in six months but barely noticed, saying that she wanted to be thinner and get a job as a fashion model. She had a flat in the large house her mother lived in, owned by her father. Occasionally he came to visit Trudy there, and each time she would be very drunk, or in a crisis, and she would rage at him for walking out on her, or ignoring her, and blame him for whatever problems were uppermost in her mind at that time. She hid her drinking from her mother, and insisted that there was nothing wrong in her life—but she knew that her mother knew, because her father had talked to her about Trudy, wanting her to get her to see sense.

The experiences of Janet, Pat, and Trudy in their early adult lives illustrate some of the common external and internal pressures which can be reasons for drinking. These can be termed *social* and *psychological* factors.

Social factors

The normally harmless, social aspects of why people drink have already been referred to—for example, relaxation, celebrations, parties, ceremonies, etc. However, there are certain aspects of drinking socially which sometimes lead to an individual drinking to excess, or in a way that leads to problems later.

'Peer pressure' is a phrase used by psychologists to describe the influence of any group of people with whom we can identify, or where we have a sense of 'belonging'. There are benefits to being part of a peer group, such as companionship, approval and security—but each member must conform to the attitudes and behaviour of the rest of the group. So, a gang of teenagers who get together to brew and drink their own beer will expect everyone in that gang to join in. Student nurses undergoing their training can be quite heavy drinkers—and Janet found that in order to be accepted by the others, she would have to drink like them. Generally amongst young, unmarried women the pressure of the group may be very powerful—whether it is a women-only or a mixed group.

For women who go out drinking with male colleagues from their place of work, the pressure may be increased because they feel they ought to 'prove themselves' to the men by drinking similar quantities.

Peer pressure and social expectations can cause problems for some drinkers when:

(1) the 'normal' amount and frequency of a group's drinking is harmful for an individual within it. For example, Janet had previously been a non-drinker and had not developed any tolerance to alcohol. When she joined in with her friends, she found that alcohol had very different effects on her from the effects on the others.

(2) an individual is too scared to—or does not know how to— refuse a drink when she feels she ought to or would like to. She might be shy or nervous, or a newcomer to the group, and is unable to resist doing what everyone else does. It is common for some people literally to not know what to say if they do not want a drink, and be unable to assert their right to drink differently from others.

(3) heavy drinkers are the only group with whom a woman feels a sense of belonging. This could be one reason why so-called 'skid row' drinkers find it very difficult to contemplate a life without drinking.

(4) when drinking in the same way as the rest of the group is in conflict with an individual's beliefs about what is right or acceptable, she becomes confused or worried. As happened with Janet, drinking larger amounts can dampen down this sort of moral discomfort—but then she felt more confused, the conflict increased, and a vicious circle was set up.

Psychological factors

The thought of having a drink is normally attractive because we expect it to have certain predictable effects. Most of these are to do with the 'drug effects' described in Chapter 2; for example alcohol makes us disinhibited, and relaxed, and alters our concentration, judgement and perceptions. All drinkers learn to associate alcohol with getting rid of or obtaining particular feelings; drinking can therefore be a deliberate decision to alter one's moods or perceptions. People in different circumstances will use it for different purposes—but this does not of course automatically mean that drinking because we want a particular effect will inevitably cause problems. But certain reasons for drinking *can* be 'danger signals', for example, if alcohol is seen as the only way of achieving a particular effect. Or the *reasons* for drinking can become the *consequences* of drinking. So, the kind of comment Trudy might make would be: 'I drink because I'm nervous, and at first that makes me more relaxed. Then I find that I need more to try to get the same feeling, and I can't relax because I know I really need that next drink. So I get agitated again, and need another drink.'

Using alcohol on certain occasions to cope with a difficult or upsetting mood or situation, or even to avoid something unpleasant, may not mean anything too sinister. But if this happens frequently, and drinking is seen to be the *only* way of coping or escaping, an unhealthy pattern is setting in.

Janet, Pat, and Trudy all used alcohol to help them relieve or cope with certain emotions and situations at certain times. Janet felt guilty after having one or two drinks because it went against her family's teetotal beliefs, and so she tried to take the edge off these feelings by drinking more. She also felt uncomfortable being different from her peers, and believed she would be more acceptable to them if she drank heavily. Pat found that increasing the amount of alcohol that she drank relieved her back pain and had beneficial side-effects: she could keep up with her boyfriend's energetic lifestyle, and she felt less depressed about the car accident in which she had been involved. Alcohol gave her a lift. For Trudy too, drinking was something 'to take her out of herself'. She felt full of anger and frustration at her father's alternating encouragment and criticism of her lifestyle. It seemed to her the only way to give vent to her feelings was to get drunk and shout or cry. When she went out, she needed something to make her feel more outgoing, more confident, and to cover up the fear of being left out and alone. It was Trudy who most often used alcohol to escape. At school she hated the boredom of weekends, and the routine and predictability of the school term. Drinking lifted her into another world. She came home in the holidays and by the age of sixteen she was drinking secretly in the garden or in her room to blot out the sound of her parent's arguments. Once she moved into her own flat, alcohol was more and more often a way of finding oblivion. There were many unpleasant emotions she didn't know how to get rid of: sadness, feeling rejected, blaming herself for her parents' divorce, worrying about her mother, anger at her father, and sometimes an overwhelming self-loathing. Janet too had times when a night's heavy drinking at a party blotted out all the insecurity and uncertainty that she felt, caught as she was between the world of her family and the world of her peer group.

Pat's, Janet's and Trudy's drinking illustrates some aspects of 'drinking for the effect'. Some psychological factors are more likely to occur amongst certain age groups or in particular circumstances, which haven't yet been described. For instance, drinking to cope with loneliness is quite common amongst isolated women with young children, or those who are disabled or elderly. Women who are bereaved may find that drinking blurs their emotional pain, and gives them a break from constantly going over the same memories and questions. For others, any major upheaval or personal crisis may lead to alcohol being either a source of comfort or an escape. Then there is the relief of stress and tension that may be sought by women who are faced with heavy demands and conflicts, because of the burdens of work within or outside their homes.

'Bout' (or 'binge') drinking

Some women's problematic drinking is confined to intermittent bouts, very often in response to an emotional crisis. These may be very occasional or quite frequent, and the feelings that trigger the bout may be a state of major distress and turmoil, or they may be a mild discomfort. Although it is difficult to collect statistics on this phenomenon, it seems that women are more prone to bout drinking than men—for instance, many women who seek help from alcohol agencies say that they have two coexisting drinking patterns: moderate or occasional drinking when they are being sociable; and 'over-the-top' drinking sessions on their own every now and then when they are emotionally stressed.

The odd 'harmless' evening of drinking 'because I'm totally fed up', can become a regular escape mechanism, and bouts can quickly increase in length and the amount consumed. The period of time between bouts may become shorter. What at first is seen as 'self-medication' becomes a frequent habit. Because the drinker may go for days, weeks, or months without an uncontrolled drinking binge, she does not regard herself necessarily as having an alcohol problem, and she may fail to make a connection between the pattern of her drinking, and all sorts of consequences such as drink/driving offences, domestic upheavals, accidents, problems at work, arguments, or health problems.

24

Drinking as a symbol

Another reason for drinking is based not on the actual effects that the drug alcohol has, but on what alcohol *represents*—its 'symbolic' power. For instance drinking whisky or brandy when it is cold and stormy outside is not because it actually warms you up (apart from an initial 'flush' which lasts a few seconds) but because it is a symbol of warmth and security. Alcohol as a symbol of festivity and celebrations is another reason for drinking, which is common to many families and cultures. These are reasons for drinking which are normally well-contained and unlikely to lead to heavy drinking or harmful consequences.

Drinking can also take on symbolic meanings in a much more personal way. These are not always obvious to the individual drinker or her family, and sometimes these can, over time, be a potentially dangerous reason for drinking. Getting drunk may, for example, be an indirect way of punishing someone else, or communicating 'a message' to them in a roundabout way. Trudy's drinking was at first a way of trying to please her parents, by being the sophisticated young woman they expected of her, while later getting drunk was a way of trying to punish her father and also trying to make him communicate with her mother in a way that made her the centre of attention. Heavy drinking may be a way of rebelling or a 'cry for help' or an angry statement—or a combination of these. Sometimes it is very difficult to understand just what the drinker is trying to say, and she herself may be full of conflicting feelings that she finds hard to express directly. It is then that a reliable 'outsider' such as a counsellor, self-help group or family therapist may be particularly helpful.

In this chapter we have looked briefly at the ways in which individuals can use alcohol for various social and psychological reasons connected to its drug effects and its symbolic nature. In the next chapter we will look in more detail at the ways in which, through their social position or roles, women may get trapped by drinking.

Janet's Drinking Diary
(for Week 1–7 April)

Day	Time	Drink	Setting	Who with/ doing what	Consequences	Money spent	Number of units
Sun 1	none—on duty						—
Mon 2	none—on duty						—
Tues 3	6–7 pm	wine	my room	with Liz— a patient had given us the bottle!	felt relaxed but a bit guilty—on duty at 7.30pm	none	3
Wed 4	10– 11pm	most of a bottle of wine	my room	by myself, letter from mum made me depressed	felt sorry for myself, cried myself to sleep	£2.00	6
Thur 5	none—day in college						—
Fri 6	9– 11pm	beer and brandy and coke	hospital social club	With Sue, Angie, Mike, Jo and Liz talking and fooling around	giggly, fell over in the car park	£5.20	8
Sat 7	9pm– 2 am	brandy, wine and punch	pub then Jo's party	party with the other students	felt good at first; self-confident, later passed out— I've forgotten what I was doing	£3.00	no idea! I guess between 10 and 15
					Total for the week		Between 27 and 32

Make yourself a set of *DRINKING DIARY* blanks to fill in for at least three weeks—preferably longer. You need to draw eight columns down and eight rows across, fill in the headings along the top and the days of the week on the left-hand side. Add up your total units each week.

4

Double standards, double problems

She has started to drink
  as a way to cope
  that makes her less able to cope

the more she drinks
the more frightened she is of becoming a drunkard

the more drunk
the less frightened of being drunk

the more frightened of being drunk when not drunk
  the more not frightened drunk
  the more frightened not drunk

the more she destroys herself
the more frightened of being destroyed by him

the more frightened of destroying him
the more she destroys herself.

From 'Knots' by R. D. Laing

There is a deep gulf between respectable, feminine behaviour and unacceptable, unfeminine behaviour and drinking to excess is regarded by society as unfeminine behaviour. It involves breaking an unwritten rule: that women should 'know their place'. 'Knowing our place' often means accepting an identity that we can't really call our own, an identity based on relationships such as wife (Mrs Jack Green) or secretary ('Hello, Mr Green's secretary speaking') or mother ('Oh you're Suzie's mother . . .'). Although there have of course been rapid changes in the last 30 years, women in public positions, particularly paid employment where they have high status, are few and far between.

Society still has very contradictory views about women: they are caricatured as scheming, virtuous, modest, vain, fragile . . . What society requires of women varies according to economic circumstances such as a country's need to have a large number of unskilled, part-time workers, and according to the individual relationships men have with the women around them. If a woman is reluctant or unable to fill society's standard picture of what she ought to be, she is regarded with suspicion, particularly in more 'traditional' families and cultures. Women are often made to feel it is their own fault if they don't fit the stereotype. They are not encouraged to wonder whether it is society's expectations that are unfair or unrealistic. Sometimes excuses are made on a woman's behalf—she has an 'inadequate' personality—or tranquillizers may be prescribed to 'help her cope'.

Society's response to women using tranquillizers, alcohol or hard drugs is influenced by stereotypes about femininity, but the links between drug use and the female role are not necessarily straightforward. Women may use these substances purely to keep abreast of the social trends around them, to be fashionable, or for their own pleasure. When the use becomes chaotic and/or frequent and/or excessive, the reasons may be connected with the struggle to suppress difficult feelings, and to try to conform to expectations about 'womanhood'. Whatever the reason, they may be looked at with pity, embarrassment, or disgust. Even tranquillizer use, although more socially acceptable amongst women, is certainly not seen as a positive aspect of being female—not in the way that heavy drinking is looked upon indulgently as a 'manly' habit amongst young single men.

Although these images of what constitutes acceptable and unacceptable femininity may sound extreme, many women believe in the stereotypes and apply them to themselves. They are quick to blame themselves for not conforming. Many women who drink heavily or who use prescribed or illegal drugs presume that 'if I can't be what my family and friends expect of me, it must be because I'm just basically no good'.

In this chapter we will look further at the kinds of pressures society puts on women, and the part alcohol may play both as a way of relieving these pressures—and increasing them. Once a woman has begun to drink more than those close to her, the social disapproval that she is likely to incur will probably make her feel guilty and ashamed, or confused, and may push her into heavier drinking, rather than acting as a limiting factor. Even though the judgements made by others may not be expressed very directly, it may trigger off embarrassment and self-doubt which she feels anyway, and this becomes a reason in itself for drinking.

Getting drunk

Getting drunk is—first and foremost—a way of 'letting go'. There are certain settings and situations where it is acceptable to drink a lot, to get loud or aggressive, and generally be irresponsible—for men. This can happen at football matches, on a Friday night in the pub, or at a bachelor party, for example. Women, however, are not welcome to participate in this sort of 'time out', nor encouraged to imitate it. A woman is expected to keep herself under control, to be responsible, and perhaps to stick to moderation 'in all things'. This is particularly true if she is a mother—she must put the needs of her family first, she should be patient and calm, she should create a harmonious environment. Being drunk conflicts with these expectations. While men are, of course, expected to be good fathers, they are at certain times (usually in a group with other men) allowed to set aside this role and be childish or even antisocial for a while. And young men without responsibilities are allowed considerable leeway about being drunk. If a woman is young and single, however, she 'ought' to be pleasant, entertaining and sexually attractive—and this means strong social pressure not to get drunk—or only to get drunk in a controlled sort of way! When a woman gets older, she mustn't get drunk because this is embarrassing to others, and conflicts with society's wish to 'keep women in their place'.

Drinking and leisure

Another possible double standard where men's and women's drinking are viewed differently is that women who drink at home may be seen as 'drinking on the job', and this is disapproved of, whereas for men drinking at home is in many cultures a normal leisure activity. Men usually have a clear separation between 'work' and 'home' but 'a woman's work is never done', as the saying goes. So women often feel bad about taking time off for themselves, and using alcohol when doing so may seem particularly self-indulgent. Going out to the pub on Saturday night or Sunday lunchtime and leaving home and the family behind may be seen as entirely acceptable for men, but rather out of character for a woman who has a home to run.

Drinking as relaxation

As alcohol has effective tranquillizing properties, to sit down with a quiet drink is a reasonable way of relaxing after a tiring day. When a woman feels that there is no harm in doing this, she is normally in company: with a friend, partner, husband, or in a pub or restaurant. However, sometimes circumstances mean her drinking alone, either because she lives by herself, or is on her own at certain times of the day. In either case, alcohol is a symbol of relaxation, perhaps a reward for having got through a difficult day—and its drug effects (slowing down the brain, muscle relaxation) are sought. A woman who is the mother of young children and/or has a job outside the home and/or takes care of elderly parents and/or does the bulk of the domestic chores, may be vulnerable to that 'quiet drink' becoming something frequent, regular, and very hard to do without. When pressures seem overwhelming, she may find that alcohol is the quickest and most accessible release, and its rewards are immediate and effective. After half a bottle of wine, or three or four glasses of sherry, the stresses of the day seem to disappear and a sort of cloak of contentment descends. Nothing seems to matter so much. Every evening, or two or three times a week, this 'treat' at the end of a stressful or monotonous day becomes a highlight that she can barely imagine doing without. The shift from an occasional way of unwinding, to drinking as the sole highspot in an exhausting day, can occur over months or years, and, although it is very understandable, it may be difficult to reverse.

Drinking to fill an emptiness

Some women will drink regularly in the evening or perhaps during the day as a reaction to loneliness—or, in contrast to the hectically busy mother or pressurized career-women, because life seems dull and unstructured. Having a drink becomes a substitute for companionship; alcohol comforts and blurs the pain of being alone. When being on one's own is not by choice, the loneliness may be tinged with sadness or anger, or a sense of helplessness. For instance children have grown up and left home, or a relationship with a lover or boyfriend has ended, or a husband or partner is often away from home, and blotting out the aloneness with a few stiff drinks becomes an attractive escape. Drinking alone means that the usual controls on the amount it is appropriate to drink on a single occasion are absent, so the social conventions of drinking at the same pace as a companion, or not getting too drunk to have a conversation, no longer apply. Drinking alone too often can make us vulnerable to drinking excessively.

The emptiness which many women seek to fill with drinking may not be as simple as lack of companionship, or bereavement. The feeling may be a deeper restlessness, a spiritual longing, or the sense of being an 'outsider'. The drinker may invest alcohol with magical qualities—it becomes more than a convenient drug; it becomes a presence, or a longed-for object. As her relationship with alcohol develops, her drinking grows into an activity which is special and jealously guarded. Sneaking drinks is part of this intensely private affair. Her relationship with alcohol is something she both loves and hates, something she feels sure that 'no-one else would understand'. She can't quite make sense of it, but she knows that it turns the emptiness and the longing into comfort. She may be aware that she has not found what she needs, but she clings to alcohol for the relief it brings. Sometimes this searching is misunderstood as being depression or boredom. The drinker herself, and anyone who may try to help her, should take account of the deeper and more complex needs which may lie at the root of this drinking.

Drinking as rebellion or escape

Men and women are taught from an early age that they ought to behave to fit comfortably into society—and it seems that women are more likely than men to blame themselves if they don't achieve this. Magazines and television programmes constantly tell us how we should improve ourselves for the benefit of husbands, our children, or our friends. We are expected to aim to be attractive, industrious, unselfish and sensitive to others' needs. While these qualities are certainly also required in men, the pressures on women to be these things are much greater. There are, of course, many women who do not have difficulties in accepting a traditional female role, or who conform happily to those personality characteristics which are seen as 'typically female'. But trying to be a superwoman, or the perfect mother or housewife, can be very stressful. Many women have mixed feelings—they want to be the kind of woman that society tells them they ought to be, because that brings the 'traditional' rewards—popularity, a husband, the approval of family and friends, but these rewards may turn sour, or be insufficient compensation for the sacrifices that have to be made. Many women feel trapped into having either to conform, or having to risk 'going it alone' and trying to discover what their unique needs and wishes are. Feeling trapped or isolated provides a strong temptation to turn to alcohol.

Getting drunk can be a 'private' or a 'public' way out—either occasionally or frequently. It may be a quiet way of seeking oblivion, shutting out confusion and frustration. Or it may be a rebellious act—stepping out of the traditional female role and at the same time not having to take full responsibility for what such a rebellion might involve. Whilst 'under the influence', a woman can forego being responsible, or sexy, or motherly, or unselfish, and also temporarily dull any guilt that might exist. It is a chance for her

31

to express parts of herself that she normally censors—she may be full of self-pity, exaggerted remorse, hate, anger, or sexual feelings. Alcohol may signify comfort or the only 'friend' who demands nothing of her.

Drinking as a sedative

Many women may start drinking alone as a form of self-medication—often using alcohol as a quick and effective sedative. The emotions that they are trying to 'bottle up' are frequently fear or anger, or a combination of these. The fear may be a realistic fear of a violent husband, or a difficult-to-deal-with relationship, where the woman seeks dutch courage so that she doesn't make herself too vulnerable. Where she feels she is powerless in a situation, for instance where she is financially dependent on a man who beats her up, drinking may become the only way for her to reduce or cope with her fear and frustration. Trying to suppress anger by drinking often occurs when a woman has been taught that expressing anger is unfeminine or wrong. She has trained herself to overlook minor irritations, or to take the blame herself if a situation is unacceptable. She is likely to have become so used to bearing responsibility herself for making things better that she loses touch with her own justifiable, or irrational anger. Over time, these unacknowledged feelings build up and women who are frequently in emotionally charged situations may turn to alcohol to help them stay calm. The danger of this way of using alcohol is that the drinker loses touch with her own capacity for expressing herself and learning to try out different ways of dealing with challenging life situations. 'Real feelings' become powerful enemies which must be kept hidden, with alcohol an ally in doing so. Even so, it is not a very trustworthy one, because often feelings escape when the drinker is drunk and she is unable to control the consequences. (See 'Moods and booze' diary, page 73.)

Identifying the situation in which our drinking occurs involves finding out more about how we feel about the roles and relationships that we have. None of us can escape completely from the stereotypes that society puts on us, and our drinking patterns may give us some clues about the way in which we manage, conform to, or rebel against these. Using alcohol as an attempt to 'escape' is understandable, but also eventually self-defeating. We need to use our understanding to move forward. For many women there is a sense of freedom in recognizing that their difficulties are not simply due to some individual inadequacy. Many of the contradictions and injustices that face women are embedded in our whole culture, and we are not the only ones to experience them. At the same time as becoming aware that we are not alone, we can also begin to discover what we share, and in what ways each of us is unique.

'Moods and booze' diary

Fill in the chart below for two weeks—or draw one up for yourself to fill in over a longer period of time. Put a tick in the box each time you drink in response to one of the following:

	M	T	W	Th	F	Sa	S	M	T	W	Th	F	Sa	S
because I felt tense														
because I felt pressurized to drink by someone else														
because I wanted to forget my worries														
because I was feeling shy or anxious														
because I felt angry														
because there was nothing else to do														
because I had to pull myself together														
because I couldn't get to sleep														
because I felt depressed														
because I felt unwell/in pain														
because I felt panicky														

This should give you a picture of the extent to which you drink for particular psychological reasons, or because you feel you can't cope. If there are more than three or four ticks each week, you are in danger of depending too heavily on alcohol.

If you regularly tick one particular reason for drinking, you should make a serious effort to deal with this mood/feeling/circumstance in an alternative way, without alcohol.

5

How much is too much?

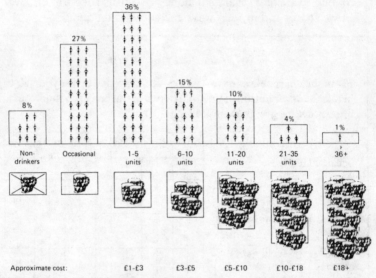

Distribution of units consumed weekly by women, England and Wales, 1984 (Source: Wallace and Haines, revised by Anderson and Jones, Oxford Alcohol Project, 1987)

Most people know that 'drinking too much is bad for you'. What is less well known is how much is 'too much' and in what ways it is 'bad'. A survey in 1982 of 2000 women in England and Wales showed that most of them knew that drinking too much could cause health problems. Many of them did not feel able to go into much detail about what the health problems might be, and when questioned in detail, a number of their guesses were inaccurate. Of those women in the survey who themselves drank up to ten units per week, the most common estimate was that women could drink up to fourteen units a week without leading to health risks. Amongst those women who drank over fifteen units per week, the estimate was in the range of a maximum of 28 units a week. This suggests that many of us can see that too much alcohol is bad for other people, but are reluctant to believe it can be bad for *me*!

Relying on alcohol

All the different aspects of a woman's life where heavy

drinking or alcohol dependence can have a damaging effect will not be examined in detail here. Each reader will need to identify for herself problem areas which only she can analyse in terms of their possible relationship to her drinking. The first question is 'to what extent does drinking dominate my life?' This sort of question, which involves thinking about the extent to which you depend on alcohol, is a complicated one, perhaps hard to answer honestly, but it is often *the* problem, a core problem, and one which overlaps with a number of other social, psychological and physical problem areas.

Alcohol dependence means that a drinker has become increasingly preoccupied with obtaining the 'good feelings' that alcohol brings, and this preoccupation will gradually mean that less time and energy is available for other things. Short-term, immediate satisfaction begins to interfere with working on long-term goals. For example, the drinker who three years ago occasionally could not make it to work on Monday mornings because she had had a heavy drinking session the previous night may now find that she is only interested in getting temporary secretarial jobs because she often feels rough in the morning and takes days off sick. The young woman whose friends used to tease her for passing out at parties now finds that recent boyfriends are constantly arguing with her about how she behaves when she has been drinking, so her relationships never last long. Getting hold of alcohol becomes increasingly important, so financial problems develop, other items are seen as less vital than alcohol for spending money on, and rows develop with family or friends.

The more entrenched the need for alcohol becomes, the more damaging dependence becomes because the drinker neglects or takes less seriously other aspects of her life. She has less money, there is more chance of trouble with the law, her employment opportunities become limited, and her physical health is vulnerable. She feels criticized about her behaviour but feels it is out of her control, and so feels increasingly guilty, and defensive. The poorer her self-esteem and the more she tries to defend herself—mainly by blaming circumstances and other people—the worse her relationships become. Her social life, family and close friendships can become increasingly fraught and unhappy, and the vicious circle of increased drinking and bad feelings continue.

Like 'dependence', there are other harmful consequences of heavy or frequent drinking which may be subtle or obvious, mild or serious. As you understand more about the effects alcohol has on the mind, and body, you will become better able to check for yourself what may apply to you. Remember that much of the damage alcohol can cause is quite separate from the phenomenon of dependence. Occasional heavy drinking sessions can lead to the drinker committing an offence, losing money, causing herself or others serious embarrassment, rows in the family, neglecting children, and problems at work. Over time, a heavy drinker may begin to define herself as having 'bad nerves': the accumulated effect of a depressant drug such as alcohol leads to suspicion, anxiety, fear, guilt, self-doubt and a sense of unhappiness. She may be diagnosed as 'depressed', when in fact a reduction or cessation of her drinking would get rid of her 'symptoms'. Taking drugs to deal with the results of heavy drinking is *extremely dangerous* because of the interaction of chemical effects, and also because the risk of suicide by an overdose of alcohol and/or drugs is much higher amongst excessive than amongst moderate drinkers.

For many reasons both drinkers themselves and the professionals who 'should know better' have been reluctant to see whether the individual's physical, social or phsychological problems can be traced to her alcohol consumption. Using a drinking diary, obtaining as much information as possible about the effects of alcohol, and examining patterns in your own lifestyle can be a positive step in making these links.

The physical effects of alcohol

It is difficult to make precise statements about the levels of drinking at which physical harm can occur. There are clearcut risks to our health if we drink large amounts in a short space of time—for instance over fifteen units in an hour could be dangerous for almost anyone. However, *one* episode of drinking smaller amounts can harm you if:

(1) You are small or light in weight.
(2) You are not 'tolerant to' alcohol.
(3) You are taking certain medication or non-prescribed drugs.
(4) Your drinking is followed by some activity which carries risks, such as driving a car.
(5) You have previously had a drinking problem which you have resolved by being abstinent.
(6) There are specific medical reasons for *not* taking alcohol.

The long-term effects on health will vary depending on a large number of factors—not just average amounts consumed per week. Medical experts cannot accurately predict how long a period of 'too much' drinking will lead to such illnesses as heart disease and cirrhosis. What is known, however, is that heavy drinking plays a major role in causing or making worse a wide variety of physical conditions.

How alcohol is absorbed

The way the body 'handles' alcohol varies from one individual to another, and there are considerable differences between men and women.

Alcoholic drinks consist of the chemical 'ethyl alcohol', water, and 'congeners' (colouring and flavouring). Alcohol is absorbed from the stomach and the small intestine into the bloodstream. How quickly this occurs would depend on how diluted the beverage is (for example, spirits are absorbed faster than beer), whether it has bubbles (for example, champagne is absorbed faster than still wine), and whether you are drinking on an empty stomach. Absorption may also be affected by mood (anxiety, for instance, may slow down absorption), expectations of the particular drinking occasion, your weight and your stage of the menstrual cycle. If alcohol is absorbed slowly, it will stay in the body for a longer time but 'peak alcohol level' (that is, intoxication) is not so quickly reached. Women absorb alcohol *more quickly* than men, and become more intoxicated because of the difference in body weight, even if they drink smaller amounts. The differences are greater during the premenstrual phase and ovulation. Women on oral contraceptives process alcohol significantly more slowly than other women, but more regularly and predictably.

Alcohol in the bloodstream

Alcohol is carried quickly by the blood to every part of the body including the brain. It affects the circulation of the blood, causing a small increase in heart rate, and it dilates blood vessels in the skin. This is sometimes misread as the warming properties of alcohol, but in fact the body temperature is *not* increased. Alcohol causes inflammation of the stomach lining and stimulates the production of gastric juices and acids, which can cause stomach or duodenal ulcers. In pregnant women alcohol crosses the placenta into the circulation of the fetus, and in breast-feeding mothers it passes into the milk.

A small amount of alcohol is excreted via the lungs, kidneys, and the skin. Most of it is broken down (metabolized) in the liver. It is while alcohol is circulating throughout the body, prior to metabol-

Blood alcohol levels

Blood alcohol level (BAL) or blood alcohol concentration (BAC) is measured according to the number of milligrams (mg) of alcohol in each 100 millilitres (ml) of blood. Thus 80 mg/per cent (which is the legal limit for driving in Britain) means that there are 80 milligrams of actual alcohol in every 100 millilitres of blood. Because women have less body fluids in which to dilute the alcohol, they are more quickly and more markedly affected than men. BAL is also affected by your weight, whether or not you have eaten and how quickly you drink.

	BAL:	Approx. 50 mg/%	Approx. 80 mg/%	Approx. 120 mg/%
Women who weigh under 57 kg (9 stones or 126 lbs)	1 hour's drinking	1½ units	2½ units	3½ units
	2 hours	2 units	3 units	4 units
	3 hours	2½ units	3½ units	4½ units
Women who weigh between 57–70 kg (9–11 stones or 126–154 lbs)	1 hour's drinking	2 units	3 units	4½ units
	2 hours	2½ units	3½ units	5 units
	3 hours	3½ units	4½ units	5½ units
Women who weigh over 70 kg (11 stones or 154 lbs)	1 hour's drinking	2½ units	3½ units	5 units
	2 hours	3 units	4½ units	6 units
	3 hours	4 units	5½ units	6½ units

BAL = 50 mg/per cent	Merry, relaxed, cheerful; slightly increased risk of accidents
BAL = 80 mg/per cent	Legal limit for driving in United Kingdom. However, the chances of having an accident are twice the no-alcohol risk level
BAL = 120 mg/per cent	Talkative, losing inhibitions, clumsy or unsteady.

ism in the liver, that 'intoxication' will occur. If you drink no faster than one unit every hour or hour and a half, alcohol will not accumulate. But the liver can only handle the breakdown and elimination of alcohol at a slow, steady rate. Thus we need to be aware that blood alcohol concentration levels may stay high for considerably longer than we realize, and will influence—amongst other things—whether we are 'over the limit' to drive. In Great Britain the legal limit for driving a car is a concentration of 80 mg of alcohol per centilitre (cl) of blood.

Blood alcohol concentration

As a rough guide, if a woman drinks 2½ pints (1·6 litres) of beer on an empty stomach, she is likely to reach a 100 mg blood alcohol concentration within a short while of finishing the second pint. Her blood alcohol level will fall by about 15 mg per 100 mls per hour, so although she may *feel* as if she is sober enough to drive, she would really need to wait at least an hour before attempting to drive home. It will be six hours from the time of starting to drink before her body is entirely alcohol-free. After a heavy drinking evening session, when the liver's speed of metabolizing lags well behind the drinker's speed of consumption, it may be the following day before there is no alcohol left in the bloodstream.

Effects on the brain

In the short term, the brain is more affected by alcohol than any other system in the body. As we have noted, by depressing the nervous system alcohol slows down our reaction times and impairs judgement. The 'disinhibition' which follows heavy drinking is not because alcohol is a stimulant, but is a result of a complex interaction between the biochemical properties of alcohol itself, and the social and cultural patterns of behaviour expected of or allowed to a drunk person. People who suppress strong emotions when sober are likely to feel less constrained and may act more impulsively—often aggressively—after drinking. Sensitivity to pain, and to discrimination in vision, hearing, odours and taste is diminished. Short-term memory, fluency and problem-solving abilities are reduced, and physical coordination is affected.

Hangovers

Hangovers are regarded by most drinkers as a sort of occupational hazard; something unpleasant which has to be tolerated in order to have the pleasure of getting drunk. In fact hangovers are a result of the congeners, the toxic properties of alcohol, its dehydrating effect, and the heightened activity of the nervous system on the 'rebound' following the depressant effect of large amounts of

39

alcohol on the brain. The toxic effects of alcohol and congeners are inevitable if large quantities are drunk, although beverages with a darker colour (such as port or red wine), which contain more congeners, tend to cause more hangover symptoms than light drinks. Dehydration occurs because alcohol acts on the hormones which control production of urine, and it alters the distribution of water in the cells of the body. Drinking a large amount of water, or diluting your alcohol generously, will reduce some hangover symptoms. Part of the hangover syndrome is like the withdrawal symptoms that occur when a drinker becomes dependent on alcohol—the nervous system adjusts to the tranquilizing effects of alcohol (or the *expectation* of these effects in the case of withdrawal symptoms) by becoming hyperactive. As the blood alcohol level drops, the person becomes restless, wakeful and uncomfortable. Taking another drink during this time is an attempt to dampen down this reaction—the 'hair of the dog' cure. This can be dangerous if it becomes a habit, a form of drinking to avoid feeling worse, rather than for a specific rewarding effect.

Hangovers do not respond well to so-called cures such as cold showers, coffee, or raw eggs. The tiredness, nausea, headaches, dizziness and possible tremulousness will subside over a period of a few hours. Hangovers are easily prevented—simply by limiting your alcohol intake—but not easily cured. And *not* getting hangovers is not a sign of a drinker's ability to cope safely with increased amounts of alcohol.

'Blackouts'

Many heavy drinkers experience 'blackouts' on certain drinking occasions, and these may occur more frequently if the number of heavy drinking sessions increases. This refers to times when behaviour which at the time appears normal (that is, the drinker seems to know what she is doing) is completely lost from conscious memory after the episode is over. This is a little understood but worrying phenomenon, usually associated with very rapid drinking. A blackout is technically referred to as 'an alcohol-related transient amnesia'.

Accidents and injuries

Many patients in the casualty departments of hospitals would not be there if they had not been drinking. More common amongst men than women, falling over, accidents with machinery, and injuries are some of the most usual problems. There are also many alarming statistics showing the relationship between road accidents and alcohol; often the blood alcohol level of an injured pedestrian, cyclist, or car passenger is high, as well as that of the car driver involved in the accident.

In England and Wales alcohol was reported as the major contributory factor in 25 per cent of deaths by drowning in 1980: it is estimated to be a higher proportion in South Africa and Australia.

In the home

In the home, alcohol was implicated in 30 per cent of fatal accidents in 1977 for the age group fifteen years and over in Britain, and in 40 per cent of deaths from fires.

Research into the link between alcohol and non-accidental injuries in the home has been somewhat neglected. However, from research in America, we know that murders committed under the influence of alcohol mainly involve acquaintances or family members. In a study of marital assaults, in 44 per cent of the cases both husband and wife had been drinking, and in a further 44 per cent only the violent spouse—almost always the man—had been drinking. In Britain, research in 1975 found that the wives of men referred to a clinic for suspected drinking problems frequently stated that violence was a problem in their marriages: 45 per cent reported being physically beaten, and another 27 per cent said that their husbands had tried to injure them. The majority had also been threatened with violence. There is some evidence that women who are beaten by their partners begin to drink heavily as a reaction, and that women who drink excessively may be attacked by their partners because of this—another vicious circle.

Child abuse

The relationship between child abuse or neglect and the parents' drinking is not clearly established. Neglect is more common than abuse in heavy drinking families, and it is more often the man's rather than the woman's drinking which is excessive. It seems that there is no reason to believe that a pattern of heavy drinking will make it more likely that a child is physically harmed, but neglect may occur when the parent is drunk and incapable.

Combining alcohol with other drugs

Combining alcohol with another drug which 'sedates' the central nervous system results in an exaggerated sedative effect, and can therefore be *extremely dangerous*. This can occur with sleeping tablets, barbiturates, tranquillizers, antidepressants, antihistamines and chlormelthiazole (Heminevrin, which is an hypnotic sometimes used in the treatment of acute withdrawal symptoms). Depression can be made worse if alcohol is taken during treatment with certain antidepressant drugs, such as imipramine hydrochloride (Tofranil) and dothiepin hydrochloride (Prothiaden).

Some drugs interfere with the metabolism of alcohol, and a toxic byproduct acetaldehyde, builds up—resulting in nausea, flushing, headache, and a fall in blood pressure. This can happen with metronidazole (Flagyl; frequently used to treat some vaginal infections), several oral antidiabetic tablets, and certain drugs specifically prescribed to discourage drinking, for example disulfiram (Antabuse).

Prolonged heavy drinking

We now turn from the acute effects of alcohol on the individual, to the problems associated with long-term (chronic) heavy drinking. Definition of terms is tricky here, but the general message is that the longer and the heavier the drinking, the more serious and the more numerous social, psychological, and physical harms are likely to become. A book published by the Royal College of Physicians in 1987 (see Appendix 2), summarizes the physical health hazards associated with alcohol abuse in a list which is almost two pages long.

The Royal College book also makes the important point that

> many individuals who are substantially harming themselves with alcohol, may show no physical, social or emotional side-effects in the early stages. It is usually only by careful questioning about alcohol intake and by measuring several biochemical and haematological markers (blood composition tests) that it is possible to identify that a disease is alcohol-related (page 2).

Effects of alcohol on the body

The brain and nervous system

Prolonged alcohol abuse can lead to brain damage in a number of ways—memory can be seriously affected, and early dementia, hallucinations and confusion may occur. Research suggests that the functioning of the brain may be harmed with a shorter history of heavy drinking for women than for men, and it has also been noted that memory and mental abilities deteriorate with prolonged use of tranquillizers and alcohol together. Another of the long-term problems which seems to be more common in women than in men is alcohol-related nerve damage, which results in 'pins and needles' or loss of sensation in fingers and toes, through to pains and difficulties in moving the limbs. There can also be weakness and swelling of the knuckles.

The liver

The liver is where some of the most serious damage can be done through excessive drinking, and women are far more vulnerable than men. One of the liver's functions is to metabolize alcohol, but if it is overworked it will fail to carry out some of its other vital and complex functions. Toxic substances such as acetaldehydes accumulate. If the liver becomes 'fatty' and enlarged there are not necessarily any symptoms, but the working of the liver is impaired. After anything between five and fifteen years of drinking, alcoholic hepatitis (inflammation) can occur and the liver develops scars. Whether or not symptoms are noticeable at this stage varies from one patient to another. A more serious condition, cirrhosis, will develop in some heavy drinkers and is associated with daily drinking of between two and five units. As frequency and quantity of drinking increases, so the risk becomes greater. Up to 10 per cent of patients with alcoholic cirrhosis will develop liver cancer at a later stage. Liver cirrhosis and cancer are likely to lead to death within a few years: for some little-understood reason, liver disease is more likely to be fatal amongst women of child-bearing age than amongst older women and men.

It appears that liver damage occurs at a lower level of regular drinking and within a shorter span of years amongst women than men. Even though drinking is not the only cause of cirrhosis, it is the most common, and evidence from all over the world shows a direct relationship between average levels of alcohol consumption, and the number of deaths from cirrhosis. Given that surveys indicate that on the whole women drink far less than men, it is worrying to note that in the United Kingdom about 40 per cent of the patients who have cirrhosis are now women. And the disease is increasing, particularly amongst black women.

The digestive system

As well as affecting the liver, alcohol can cause serious damage, including cancer, to the oesophagus—the tube leading from the mouth to the stomach. The risk of developing cancer of the oeseophagus is eighteen times more likely amongst heavy drinkers (over ten units a day) and 44 times more likely if these drinkers also smoke 20 cigarettes or more a day. In smaller quantities, drinking can lead to inflammation and bleeding of the oeseophagus. It also affects the pancreas, causing inflammation, which can lead to chronic damage, giving rise to intense pain, and can sometimes lead to diabetes. The longer the period of heavy drinking, the higher the risk of developing chronic pancreatitis—some research found ten to twelve years to be the average for women.

More common problems for heavy drinkers are acute gastritis (stomach pains) and diarrhoea. Alcohol may aggravate or slow down the healing of ulcers in the stomach and duodenum. Gastritis usually heals within a few days of abstinence.

Two effects of heavy drinking on the body which are not generally well known are malnutrition, and how alcohol affects weight. Alcohol contains many calories (one gin and tonic has about 150 calories, roughly the same as a large ice-cream) and few nutrients, and as the drinker *increases* her intake, she is likely to decrease her intake of nutritional food. She may lose her appetite, but—in the early stages of heavy drinking—put on weight. Later, however, there is weight loss, and the muscles become weaker, bones lose their mineral content, and vitamins are not properly used. The body's ability to withstand physical stress and infections is reduced because of this malnutrition. Reducing alcohol intake and improving nutrition (including taking extra vitamins) has been found to accelerate improvement in patients with alcohol-related liver damage, and increase their survival. When malnutrition is reversed, some alcohol-related brain damage and impaired memory and judgement has been found to improve.

The heart and blood pressure

Heavy drinking appears to cause damage to the heart muscles, but perhaps affects women less than men. It is not a specific 'risk factor' for coronary heart disease, but someone who has failing heart muscle should abst: in from alcohol completely. Apparently healthy drinkers and chronic alcohol abusers have occasionally been found to have abnormal heart rhythms after a binge but it is unclear whether this is linked to long-term harm.

In the late 1970s it was found that amongst patients with high blood pressure, heavy drinking was the most frequent underlying cause that could be identified. Reducing drinking leads to an almost

Approximate calorie values

Drink	Approximate calories
1 unit sherry	60–70
1 unit whisky (neat)	60–90
1 glass of wine	60–90
1 unit of brandy (neat)	75
½ pint (250 ml) beer	80–150
½ pint (250 ml) lager or cider	100–180
½ pint (250 ml) 'special' lager	200
½ pint (250 ml) stout (for example, Guinness)	210
1 vodka and orange	130
1 gin and tonic	140

immediate drop in blood pressure. A large research study in the United States found that 20 per cent of people drinking fifteen units a day had raised blood pressure (both males and females). Amongst people who have a stroke, excessive drinking is likely to have played a part.

Drinking and reproduction

Apart from experiments on rats, there has not been much research into the effects of alcohol on the female reproductive system as a whole. It has been shown that heavy drinking has a toxic effect on human hormones that stimulate various glands, including the pituitary, which in turn produces hormones that affect ovulation. It is assumed that this may be responsible for a higher rate of infertility than average amongst women with alcohol problems. There is also some evidence that the female sex hormone oestradiol is reduced in women drinkers, and when the ovaries fail to function properly, menstrual problems and sexual difficulties may occur. However, all these findings have been disputed, and the harzardous amount or length of drinking is seldom clear from the research. It is not known whether abstinence from alcohol reverses the effects on the reproductive system.

Regarding the consequences of moderate drinking on fertility, a recent survey has shown men to be at risk at levels of four to six units of alcohol a day. At a male infertility clinic, 40 per cent of those attending were thought to have a low sperm count as a result of their drinking. The sperm count returned to normal after three months of abstinence in half of these patients. There has not been a similar study on women.

Many studies show that women who are chronic heavy drinkers are more likely than others to experience premenstrual tension, miscarriages, hysterectomies and sexual problems. Not much progress has been made in establishing whether the heavy drinking leads to, or is a result of, these difficulties. Certainly a large proportion of women identify the premenstrual phase as the time when they are more likely to drink heavily, or restart drinking after a period of abstinence.

Effects of alcohol on the fetus

This has been a popular area of discussion—even panic—during the last fifteen years. However, the focus of research and debate has been almost entirely on the mother's drinking during pregnancy, with only a small number of studies investigating the effect on the fetus, or the newborn, of the parents' drinking prior to conception. It has been found that the birthweights of babies born to women with a history of alcoholism, who abstained during pregnancy, were on average lower than the birthweights of the babies born to a group of non-alcoholic women who drank very little during pregnancy, but were higher than the birthweight of babies born to women who continued to drink.

There seems to be very little scientific interest in the contribution of heavy drinking fathers (much of the research which exists was done on animals). One study of 22 families with an alcoholic father and non-alcoholic mother found that children conceived during the father's heavy drinking period showed poorer intellectual ability than children conceived when he was abstinent or drinking moderately. Lower birthweights of the babies of heavy drinking fathers have also been reported. Possible causes of this are not yet established.

In spite of popular interest, there is still somewhat confusing information available about safe or harmful levels of drinking for the mother during pregnancy. Many women reduce their drinking automatically during their pregnancy. The vast majority of newly pregnant women will not need the warnings of health workers about risks associated with drinking while pregnant, because they develop a distaste for alcohol (along with other toxic substances such as tobacco and caffeine). This usually occurs in the first three months, but levels of consumption remain low thereafter.

Fetal alcohol syndrome

The 1987 report of the Royal College of Physicians on the medical consequences of alcohol abuse (see Appendix 2) points out that smoking and illegal drugs are more likely to cause harm to the growing fetus than moderate drinking. They state that 'there is no conclusive evidence that alcohol ingestion at moderate levels, that is less than ten units per week (80 mg) at the time of conception or during pregnancy results in an adverse fetal outcome'. The *fetal alcohol syndrome* refers to a cluster of characteristics including low birthweight, distinctive facial features, neurological problems, hyperactive behaviour and intellectual impairment seen in a small proportion of the offspring of heavy drinking women. Some research indicates that it tends to occur amongst women who drink even *moderate* amounts during pregnancy. It is fairly rare in Britain, so far having been seen in less than one in every 1000 births. Lesser forms of harm—'fetal alcohol effects'—may occur more often than the full syndrome. These effects include learning difficulties, behavioural problems, retarded growth, and some minor and major congenital abnormalities.

Spontaneous abortion

Some research suggests that the risk of spontaneous abortion increases amongst women who drink at least two units twice per week; and women drinking between seven and fourteen units a week in the first three months of pregnancy are twice as likely to miscarry, but why only some pregnancies are affected is not understood. The precise role alcohol plays is unclear, but if these statistics are accurate and can be generalized, it seems that this would be a straightforward reason for radical reduction in alcohol intake during pregnancy. It is perhaps for this reason that the Royal College of Physicians report sticks to the conservative recommendation that 'it is probably sensible for women planning a pregnancy, or currently pregnant, to abstain from alcohol, or at least to restrict their consumption to an occasional drink, especially in the early stages of pregnancy' (page 95).

Drugs and prolonged alcohol use

As a large proportion of women who take tranquillizers regularly also drink heavily 'cross-addiction' can often occur: when the drinker reduces her alcohol intake she can avoid withdrawal symptoms by continuing or increasing her consumption of tranquillizers—or vice versa. When tolerance occurs to one drug, she will develop tolerance to the other. This can be very dangerous in that the drinker continues to take large amounts of alcohol and/or other drugs in order to feel intoxicated, without realizing the potential there is for physical harm. It seems that minimal brain damage (for example, reduced intellectual ability and poor memory) is widespread amongst young women who combine tranquillizers with moderate or heavy drinking over a number of years.

It does appear that in spite of women's overall lower consumption, there are certain risks attached to being a female drinker, as far as health is concerned. A number of aspects of the long-term effects for the body are controversial, unclear and poorly researched. It is the responsibility of women drinkers themselves, those in medical and related professions, and society as a whole, gradually to reduce our ignorance, in order to promote healthy and clear guidelines about drinking.

Talking to your doctor

The often hidden connection between the amount someone drinks and the way it is affecting her physically is a subject not much talked about. We are not educated at home or at school about the damage alcohol can cause to the individual drinker, in anything like the way that recently smoking and illegal drugs have been highlighted. The woman visiting her family doctor with complaints of non-specific pains, sleeplessness, depression or other symptoms is not always encouraged to consider whether these are linked with her drinking. The doctor himself or herself may not have had adequate training in making possible connections, as this has only recently begun to be emphasized in the training of general practitioners. Also, there may be embarrassment and fear—the doctor does not wish to appear inappropriately inquisitive, or judgemental, or he/she cannot believe that a particular female patient could have an alcohol problem. The patient in her turn doesn't necessarily volunteer information about her drinking, and is worried about what her doctor may think of her! A conspiracy of silence can mean that reversible physical harm stays undetected and the problems become worse.

Patients can take the initiative in (a) discussing their own drinking and 'safe limits' with their doctor; (b) asking for specific tests to be done to detect liver damage; (c) checking whether alcohol should be avoided with certain prescribed medication.

You could take with you to a consultation a drinking diary

covering a few weeks, or a record of your weekly consumption over a month or two, and discuss with your doctor increases or changes in your drinking habits in the past one to five years. Write down the questions you want to ask. You may wish to make statements like: 'I'm not sure whether to be worried about my drinking or not. Perhaps if I tell you the sort of amount I've been drinking in recent months you could tell me whether it may have something to do with the sleeplessness (stomach pains, forgetfulness, high blood pressure, etc.) that I have been talking about.' Don't assume that your doctor has all the answers, but do keep him or her informed about your drinking. It's often useful to seek counselling or information from an alcohol advice agency as well as getting in touch with your doctor.

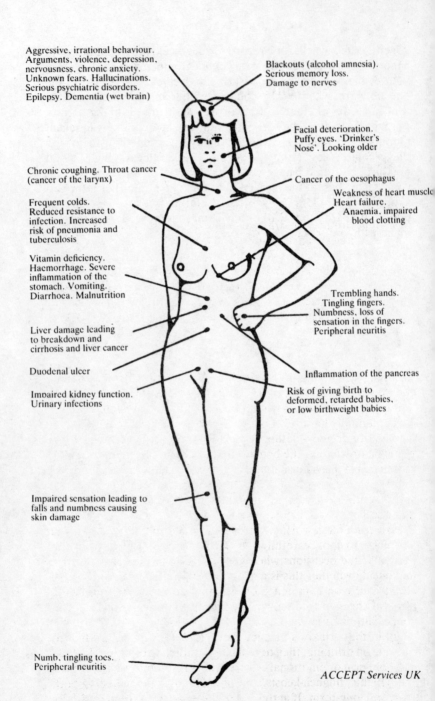

Aggressive, irrational behaviour. Arguments, violence, depression, nervousness, chronic anxiety. Unknown fears. Hallucinations. Serious psychiatric disorders. Epilepsy. Dementia (wet brain)

Blackouts (alcohol amnesia). Serious memory loss. Damage to nerves

Facial deterioration. Puffy eyes. 'Drinker's Nose'. Looking older

Chronic coughing. Throat cancer (cancer of the larynx)

Cancer of the oesophagus

Weakness of heart muscle. Heart failure. Anaemia, impaired blood clotting

Frequent colds. Reduced resistance to infection. Increased risk of pneumonia and tuberculosis

Vitamin deficiency. Haemorrhage. Severe inflammation of the stomach. Vomiting. Diarrhoea. Malnutrition

Trembling hands. Tingling fingers. Numbness, loss of sensation in the fingers. Peripheral neuritis

Liver damage leading to breakdown and cirrhosis and liver cancer

Duodenal ulcer

Inflammation of the pancreas

Impaired kidney function. Urinary infections

Risk of giving birth to deformed, retarded babies, or low birthweight babies

Impaired sensation leading to falls and numbness causing skin damage

Numb, tingling toes. Peripheral neuritis

ACCEPT Services UK

WHERE ALCOHOL MISUSE TAKES ITS TOLL

6

Stopping and cutting down

So far we have looked at the background to 'normal' and heavy drinking, considering the influence of families and society generally, some of the reasons why women drink, and the effects of alcohol. You will have begun to think about your own drinking. Not everyone needs to make major changes in the quantities or patterns of their drinking—indeed, statistics show that the majority of women in Britain who drink seldom exceed suggested 'safe limits'. And only a very small minority of women drink in a way which indicates that they should seriously consider stopping altogether. Nevertheless, for those like Janet, Pat and Trudy who decide to cut down or cut out drinking, the following chapters offer some guidelines. The decisions that need to be made concern goals, and the means of reaching them.

Is it worth it?

Drinking alcohol has both costs and benefits, as we have seen from the previous five chapters. The drinking patterns of Janet, Pat and Trudy all included times when alcohol was useful, and times when it was potentially harmful. Like any activity in which we participate, we need to decide whether the costs of that activity outweigh the benefits, or whether the benefits are worth the costs. For example, taking up playing squash may bring us companionship and improve our fitness, but we may stop playing (or play less often) if the nearest sports centre closes down, and we have to travel a long distance to find another squash court.

To consider 'is it worth it?' to change your drinking activities, you will need to look carefully at your drinking diary. Consider in particular the occasions when your drinking has led to problems, and decide whether this is a common pattern. As well as thinking about your own experience of drinking, you may wish to have a physical checkup to discover any negative consequences as far as your health is concerned.

Fill in the 'drinker's balance sheet' (below) with regard first to carrying on drinking, then to reducing or stopping drinking. Include psychological or emotional costs and benefits, family or social costs and benefits, financial costs, and physical costs and benefits—both short and long-term. If at the end of this exercise you can truthfully

A balance sheet: the costs and benefits of drinking

Draw up a 'balance sheet' for yourself and first of all fill in what you believe to be the costs (or disadvantages) and the benefits (or advantages) of your drinking, as it is now. Think about both the immediate consequences and the long-term ones. Then imagine that you were *either* going to reduce your drinking, *or* stop completely. Fill in what you imagine the immediate and long- term costs and benefits would be.

In each box, consider each of the following aspects:

emotional	work
relationships/family	money
social life	health

	Costs	*Benefits*
To carry on as I am now		
To stop or reduce my drinking		

	Costs	*Benefits*
To carry on as I am now	makes me feel guilty makes mum and dad have a go at me too many rows with friends hangovers headaches and can't get to sleep I might lose my driving licence	helps me relax makes me more confident gives me oblivion
To stop drinking	I'd get more depressed I'd have no way of unwinding I'd have nothing to look forward to my friends would think I was crazy	I'd have more energy I'd get into fewer arguments I'd have more money I wouldn't get hung over

TRUDY'S BALANCE SHEET: WHEN SHE WAS 20 YEARS OLD

say to the best of your knowledge that the benefits of carrying on drinking outweigh the disadvantages, it is unlikely that you will feel particularly motivated to reduce or stop your drinking. If there is any doubt in your mind about your ability to do this exercise honestly, or if you are unsure which way the balance lies, ask someone you trust to go through the exercise with you.

Can I do it?

You may well say that you can recognize that you *ought* to change your drinking, but you're not sure that you can. The questions 'am I worth it?' and 'can I do it?' focus on self-confidence and a belief in our own ability. Women who have tried and failed in the past to change something, may be doubtful about being able to succeed in the future. Other people have told them that they are indecisive, lacking in willpower, or simply not very good at getting things done, and they may have started to believe it themselves. And yet most of us have in fact succeeded in sticking to certain resolutions, breaking a habit, or pursuing some new activity at some time. Think back over those types of situations or activities. Write down everything you can remember about how you managed to make and stick to a constructive decision, including the following:

(1) What were the circumstances leading up to the decision?
(2) Were you the only one making such a decision?
(3) Did you believe you could do it?
(4) What 'techniques' did you find were most helpful in keeping you going?
(5) What did you do when you were tempted to give up the new behaviour or resolution?
(6) What rewards were there?

Then consider carefully which answers are now relevant to a decision to change your drinking.

Sometimes we don't choose to make a change in our behaviour or lifestyle, it just happens. People adjust to new situations or new ways of doing things, such as living in a new town, or bringing up a child, by using various 'coping strategies'. For example, we get in touch with other people who have been through the same problem and swap notes, or we get hold of information, and if things are going badly we tell ourselves that it is probably temporary and things will get better. These strategies are ways of coping with a new and different situation, and may be useful to you in realizing how you could cope with new drinking habits, or abstinence. If you have not got a previous experience of trying to change some behaviour, write down the strategies that you have used to adjust to any new set of circumstances in your life. It is likely that you will be able to identify positive things that you did, as well as ways in which you tried to *think* more positively about your situation.

Am I worth it?

As well as believing that you have the capacity to achieve a new goal, you also will need to have the sense that you are 'worth fighting for'. Self-confidence is about the image you have of yourself, as well as your belief in your own skills or abilities. Heavy drinking may result in losing a belief in your ability to cope with situations, and it can also lead you to label yourself as a person who 'can't cope'. In the short-term, alcohol, as we have seen, can be an anaesthetic or a pick-me-up. As time goes by, the belief that 'alcohol will help me cope with this particular difficulty' becomes a belief that 'alcohol helps me cope most of the time', and then 'I can't cope without alcohol'. From this set of beliefs, a more destructive belief may emerge, and that is '. . . and therefore I'm a loser . . .'. The drinker who views herself in this way is likely to 'resign herself' to being the kind of person who 'may as well drink herself to death'. The prospect of cutting down or stopping drinking is dismissed as pointless: 'who cares if I die of liver cirrhosis? I don't!'. The bigger the part drinking plays in your life, the less room is left for *you*.

All of us may feel a sense of worthlessness at some time in our lives. The idea that we should have personal responsibility for keeping ourselves healthy, or caring for our own emotional well-being, seems hollow. Trying to convince ourselves that we have a right to be reasonably happy, or to be in control of our own lives, can sometimes seem meaningless. We may even become resentful at any suggestion that this is possible or desirable. Heavy drinking can be a way of perpetuating this. Some women even find a kind of security in constantly reminding themselves that they are failing to control their drinking, and therefore they must be a failure. It is a self-defeating vicious circle, hard to break out of. Even so, facing up to the image that we have of ourselves can play a big part in the decision to stop or reduce our drinking.

Alcohol as we know, distorts our judgement, and over time you may have lost the capacity to see yourself except in very extreme terms. It may have formed a protective barrier between you and other people, preventing you from picking up feedback from them. This increases isolation and leaves you stuck with assumptions about being worthless or hopeless, which you never question. Even a short alcohol-free period of time will enable you to see yourself in a more balanced way.

'Am I worth it?' will have different answers according to circumstances at different times of our lives. We will feel better about ourselves when we are doing work that we enjoy and feel rewarded for, or when we are in a close or trusting relationship. We find it easier to 'believe in' ourselves when someone who we have faith in, believes in us. This may be our family, a lover, a close friend, a counsellor or therapist, or a group. Making a decision to become less self-destructive is strengthened when we have another person's support. This support cannot be a substitute for our own sense of being a worthwhile person, but it can provide encouragement and a nudge in the right direction.

Some people say that for a woman who is severely dependent on alcohol, a decision to change will only occur when she has reached 'rock bottom'. At this point she can no longer avoid making links between certain problems in her life and her drinking. The costs clearly outweigh the benefits, often quite suddenly, and she is forced to reflect honestly on her situation. She may feel full of self-hatred, and hopelessness, but this may be precisely the point at which she stops putting on a brave face, and making half-hearted attempts to change, which she has no confidence in. She is vulnerable because she has no defences left. If you are at this point, 'surrender' may indeed be appropriate; this means surrendering to the need for help from others, from which point you can build up a sense of your own worth. You need to seek out an individual (someone you know and trust, or a specialist 'helper') or a group, or go to an alcohol 'helping agency', who can offer you safety and support as you come to terms with negative and positive views about yourself and the possibility of change. This can be a break in a downward spiral, and is likely to turn into an upward spiral, as you discover that change is not only possible, but brings rewards both from others and yourself.

Avoiding change

One of the most tricky things about being very dependent on something or someone, is that it is not always obvious to the person who is dependent. Other people may recognize the dependency more easily. Also, habits and 'dependencies' can creep up on us gradually, and we have no reason to notice that they are there. For instance, many couples are very interdependent, and only notice this when their partner is away from home, or for some reason they are left to cope alone. Often a man who regards himself as very independent would find it very hard to admit the extent of his dependence on his wife. In spite of it being obvious to other people, if having to 'admit to' this state of affairs implies that the man is not fully in control of his life, he is likely to be even more reluctant to do so. If such a person is concerned about keeping up a good image of himself, he may disagree with the observations of others, and see them as criticisms.

When it comes to dependence on alcohol, similar psychological processes can occur. We need to look more closely at why some drinkers find it so difficult to recognize and tackle the extent of their dependence on drinking.

First, like being dependent on another person, alcohol dependence implies suffering discomfort in its absence. The more severe the dependence, the more severe the discomfort. For a drinker who has not had to do without alcohol often enough to experience discomfort, the dependence is never fully exposed. For instance, a woman who drinks heavily but who has had a period of abstinence may have been given tranquillizers at this time, which masked or completely removed any withdrawal symptoms. She can therefore state that she does not believe that she is dependent on alcohol.

Second, dependence does not happen overnight. Drinking may gradually begin to play a more and more important part in a woman's life, but she would be hard put to it to say exactly when she could no longer imagine her social life without heavy drinking being part of it. Tolerance to alcohol also develops gradually, as does the compulsion and craving of 'just another one or two'. Others may be able to notice these things but the drinker herself may find it very hard to identify such changes.

Third, the severely dependent drinker may not have made the link between some of the problems that have been occurring in her life, and the pattern and quantity of her drinking. For example, the fact that her teenage daughter doesn't spend any time at home is blamed on adolescent rebellion, and she does not recognize that her daughter avoids being in the house whenever and because her mother is drinking heavily. All kinds of consequences of her dependence on alcohol are misread by her, and seem to be *reasons* for drinking—feeling tired and depressed, the family being unsupportive to her, or no longer getting a 'lift' after just two or three drinks.

Fourth, as other people start to notice the drinker's preoccupation with drinking and the difficulties it leads to, they may point this out. This is usually regarded by the drinker as a criticism or attack. A perfectly normal reaction for any of us when we feel we are being attacked, is to defend ourselves—either by arguing that the criticism is untrue or unjustified, or by retaliating. This is very common for severely dependent drinkers. When the drinker has an image of herself as 'coping' with her drinking, she will be particularly sensitive to any hint from other people that she is not in fact coping at all. In addition, she will regard any criticism of her behaviour as a potential threat to the very behaviour that helps her deal with criticism—in other words, her escape to alcohol.

In our society, being 'in control of things' and 'indepedent' are admired qualities, and someone who becomes dependent on, say, alcohol or another drug, is expected to be ashamed of this fact. Even though women's dependence on men is regarded as a fact of contemporary life, there are contradictory messages in contemporary society, which tell young women in particular that they should be able to be self-dependent. The conflicts that this can cause are little tolerated, and the use of a mood-altering substance is regarded with suspicion unless it is recommended by a doctor, such as being prescribed a tranquillizer. It is no wonder that 'dependence' and 'denial' so often go together.

It may be that you are one of those heavy drinkers who has a constant battle inside your head; one side privately believing that alcohol is causing problems, and the other side contradicting this. To allow the side that 'recognizes' alcohol-related problems to win would mean facing the possibility of giving up drinking, and thereby risking the discomfort and insecurity of not having the bottle to depend on. Thus it is tempting to try to shout down or ignore anyone else who tries to 'get you to admit to your alcohol problems', even though deep down inside part of you agrees with the need to make some changes.

You may be wondering what all this has to do with goal-setting. Choosing an appropriate goal has to be a careful, rational decision and for many drinkers this won't be too difficult to do. However, the drinker who is nearer the 'severe dependence' end of the spectrum, might find it very hard to deal with the conflicting messages that she gives herself about her drinking, and therefore will not find it easy to establish a goal which is beneficial, realistic and specific. She may avoid facing up to the 'out of control' feelings which thinking about drinking stirs up in her. If this applies to you, you may feel panicky, guilty and confused, and there is a danger you will be tempted to say 'I'll try and cut down' and then when this fails, to give up trying. You are more likely to succeed if you set yourself an abstinence goal, and seek the help of a counselling agency or Alcoholics Anonymous.

What kind of drinker?

1. If I was advised to give up drinking for the sake of my health:
   - (a) I could do so easily
   - (b) I could do so but I'd miss it
   - (c) I could do so but with difficulty
   - (d) I could only do so if I had help
   - (e) I don't think I could do it

2. This time last year my favourite drink was:
   - (a) stronger than what I drink now
   - (b) weaker than what I drink now
   - (c) the same as what I drink now

3. When I am drinking with my friends I notice that:
   - (a) they seem to drink about the same speed as I do
   - (b) they drink faster than I do
   - (c) some of them drink slower than I do
   - (d) most of them drink slower than I do

   If you answered 'yes' to (a) or (b) please answer the following:
   - (e) I have changed my friends
   - (f) I have kept my old friends

   If you answered 'yes' to (e) then please answer the following:
   My new friends:
   - (g) drink faster than my old friends
   - (h) drink slower than my old friends

4. Where I buy my drink:
   - (a) I have a credit account
   - (b) I do not have a credit account

   If you answered 'yes' to (a) then please complete the following:-
   The amount that I owe on my credit account is:
   - (c) generally about what I'd expect
   - (d) sometimes rather more than I'd expected

5. I usually first think about drinking:
   - (a) when I wake up
   - (b) some time during the morning
   - (c) at lunchtime
   - (d) late in the afternoon
   - (e) in the evening

   If you answered 'yes' to (a), (b), or (c) then please answer the following:
   When I plan the rest of my day:
   - (f) drinking is a high priority
   - (g) drinking is not particularly important to me

6. Before going to a social event:
   - (a) I never have a drink
   - (b) I seldom have a drink
   - (c) I usually have a drink

7. When I decide whether to go to a social event:
   - (a) It doesn't matter to me whether or not alcohol is going to be available there
   - (b) I prefer some drink to be available there
   - (c) I don't really enjoy it unless some drink is going to be available
   - (d) I will only attend if I know drink will be available there

8. After I have had a few drinks:
   - (a) I never pretend that I've had less to drink that I really have
   - (b) I occasionally do pretend that
   - (c) I often do pretend that
   - (d) I sometimes declare one more drink than I've actually had

9. When it gets towards closing time:
   - (a) I find I've had enough to drink
   - (b) I tend to double my final order or buy some to take home with me

continued

10. In the course of everyday conversation my friends:

(a) seldom talk about drinking

(b) quite often talk about drinking

If you answered 'yes' to (b) then please also answer the following:

I have noticed that my friends usually:–

(c) joke about it

(d) offer some kind of advice to me

(e) talk about drinking much more than me

Add up your score as follows:

1 (a)=1	3 (a)=1	5 (a)=4	7 (a)=1	9 (a)=1
(b)=1	(b)=1	(b)=3	(b)=2	(b)=3
(c)=2	(c)=2	(c)=2	(c)=3	
(d)=3	(d)=3	(d)=1	(d)=4	
(e)=4	(e)=2	(e)=1		
	(f)=1	(f)=3		
	(g)=4	(g)=1		
	(h)=2			

2 (a)=1	4 (a)=2	6 (a)=1	8 (a)=1	10 (a)=1
(b)=3	(b)=1	(b)=2	(b)=3	(b)=2
(c)=2	(c)=1	(c)=3	(c)=4	(c)=3
	(d)=2		(d)=2	(d)=4
				(e)=1

SCORING

Under 17: You have no immediate cause for concern. But remember that drinking behaviour may change over time and at other times in your life your habits and attitudes could be quite different.

18–24: You are mildly vulnerable to losing control over your drinking, and you may experience a 'need' to drink—this is not likely to happen very often, nor to be particularly strong. Combined with a moderate or high weekly alcohol intake, you could get yourself or others into difficulties caused by your drinking.

25–30: If you are in this category, you are probably drinking regularly and frequently. The amount you drink is likely to be higher than recommended limits, and harm to yourself or others probably occurs. You may not at present recognize that some difficulties are drink-related, and invisible health problems may be developing. The need to drink—your dependence on drinking—may not be recognized because regular drinking prevents you from noticing it.

Over 30: If or when you stop drinking for a short period of time, you probably experience quite a lot of psychological and physical discomfort. You are likely to be drinking fairly large quantities on a regular basis, and various physical, psychological and social problems are developing. You have probably developed considerable tolerance to alcohol.

7

Setting goals

Once you have decided that you are ready to make some changes, you will want to consider whether drinking less, or not drinking at all, is the best goal for yourself. The amount per day or per week that you aim to drink will be most important, but don't forget to think about the pattern of your drinking as well.

Goals

Reduced consumption

Many women will simply wish to limit their drinking to a quantity and pattern which makes immediate or future problems unlikely. This may be done by cutting down straight away or gradually, and ensuring that you are flexible about the reasons for your drinking and its circumstances (that is, where, when, how, and who with).

You will need to set a specific long-term goal (for example, 'by the 31st of next month I will be drinking less than fifteen units per week, and I shall have two alcohol-free days a week') and short-term objectives ('I will not drink more than three units per day for the next two weeks'). After the long-term goal has been reached you are likely to be less self-conscious about your drinking, and you will have regulated your consumption patterns so that your normal social drinking will be at a lower level than previously.

Controlled drinking

This is of course similar to the idea of reduced consumption, but its goal is a rather stricter way of viewing one's drinking. 'Controlled drinking' implies that all future drinking must follow certain rules—about the way of drinking as well as the amount. For instance, controlled drinking may include such safeguards as 'I will not drink on my own' and 'I will never drink before 6.00 pm'. It is usually an appropriate goal for the drinker who says 'yes, my drinking has been somewhat out of control, but I have been able to drink at a sensible level for long periods of time in the past'.

If you set yourself a long-term goal of controlled drinking, you should set yourself an interim goal of a period of abstinence, of anything between two weeks and three months. This will enable you to break your past habits more easily, give your body a chance to recover physically, and enable you to prove to yourself that alcohol is not ruling your life. (If you are able to achieve an initial period of abstinence satisfactorily, and you find this to be physically or emotionally rewarding, you may want to consider this as a long-term goal, instead of just a temporary one.)

A controlled drinker is similar to the person who has a tendency to be overweight, who after having dieted and reached a target weight, thereafter keeps a watch on her eating pattern, setting herself limits about the amount and types of food she will eat, and monitoring her calorie intake.

Total abstinence

There is some difference of opinion about who should aim for a goal of total abstinence, and this is discussed more fully later. However, it is generally agreed to be a good idea for the following categories of people:

(1) Anyone who has in the past been abstinent for an extended period of time and has found this satisfying and problem-free.
(2) Anyone who is *severely dependent* on alcohol—in particular anyone who regularly experiences withdrawal symptoms such as shaking, sweating, nausea and agitation after stopping drinking.
(3) Anyone with serious alcohol-related medical problems, for example liver damage, pancreatitis, or brain damage, or other health problems which may be made worse by moderate drinking.
(4) Anyone who is a member of Alcoholics Anonymous, or who finds the 'disease model' of alcohol personally appealing.
(5) Anyone who at present regards drinking as their *only* way of coping with or escaping from ongoing emotional difficulties. (In this case, positive steps should be taken to change one's circumstances, or seek appropriate help, in order to deal with these difficulties, at the same time as cutting out drinking completely.)

As there are still many unanswered questions about why severe dependence or 'alcoholism' occurs in some people and not others, there is also continuing debate about whether or not *anyone* who is having difficulties with their drinking should try to reduce or control their consumption, or whether they should abstain completely. There has always been argument about how to define 'alcoholism'. Alcoholics Anonymous regard alcoholism as a disease, and two things follow from this: first, the person who suffers from alcoholism will have this for life, and can never relearn moderate drinking habits; second, 'alcoholics' are qualitatively different from 'heavy drinkers' and 'problem drinkers'. They believe that there is something different in terms of their biology and the way they cope with alcohol, both physically and emotionally, and that until this physiological aspect is better understood it is best to regard alcoholics as 'allergic' to alcohol. While this is a well-respected viewpoint amongst many treatment agencies and the general public, it may put some women off taking their drinking seriously, because they fear that if they recognize *anything* harmful, heavy, or dependent about their drinking, their only option is to stop altogether.

If you are interested in exploring the different attitudes to alcoholism and problem drinking more deeply, you should consult some of the books recommended in Appendix 2.

General goal-setting guidelines

Now that you are at a decision-making stage consider the following guidelines. Remember that the decision to change is entirely yours, and *you* have to take responsiblity for following through your course of action.

Reaching a goal should bring benefits or rewards

Goals should not be just what we 'ought' to do, but should incorporate a sense that we *want* to do something. Reducing or cutting out alcohol will bring its own rewards: feeling fitter, being healthier, having better powers of concentration and quicker reactions, and having more spare cash. You will also know of specific psychological, social or physical consequences that are unique to you. As a bonus, you may find it useful to make a contract with someone, agreeing on a 'treat' which you can be assured of getting when you reach your final goal.

Goals should be realistic

Don't get too carried away by the idea of turning over a new leaf or wiping the slate clean; progress may be slower than you had hoped, and you are unlikely to have an overnight personality change! Don't underestimate just how strong a habit can be. In any given week there may be unusual circumstances which make you feel more pressurized than you had expected, or situations may arise which catch you offguard. It is wise to set goals which are easy to reach in the early stages of changing your behaviour, rather than trying to aim for perfection straight away. If your goal is abstinence, it is realistic and helpful to see yourself as having a *daily* goal to achieve—'just for today I won't have a drink'. If you are trying to make a number of changes in your life at the same time, these should complement each other, for example getting more exercise and cutting down your drinking may go together well—but this may not be a good time also to go on a diet.

Being realistic about your goals also means being self-confronting and honest. The opinion of someone you trust should be sought if you are in two minds about whether to abstain, reduce or aim for controlled drinking.

Another vital aspect of setting realistic goals is that you should review your goals at regular intervals, in the light of your own experience, changes in circumstances, or new information (such as about your health). For instance, the 'controlled drinker' who starts a new job working at a restaurant, might find it easier to stop drinking completely (and identify herself as an 'abstainer') than to have to monitor her alcohol consumption all the time.

Goals should be specific and measurable

If someone is trying to lose weight, they will be more successful if she says 'I want to lose 10 lbs (4½ kg) before I go on holiday' than if she says 'I want to be thin and beautiful by the summer'. Similarly the drinker needs to set a specific, measurable target so she can tell whether or not it has been achieved by a certain date. You may start the goal-setting process by thinking of 'the ideal you', but you will need to translate this ideal into a *behaviour*. Thus, 'I'd like to be really relaxed about my drinking, and never go to extremes' needs to be broken down into a set of rules or guidelines, such as

(1) I will not drink at all with my in-laws or any of my colleagues at work, as they make me feel nervous and I often try to drink at the same speed as them.
(2) I will only drink low alcohol beer or shandy when I am in a pub because I feel full after two pints, and I don't get giggly or stupid on that amount of alcohol.
(3) My weekly limit will be fourteen units up until 31st January, then I will review the situation.

You need short-term objectives as well as long-term goals

As discussed in Chapter 5, a single 'session' of drinking can be dangerous if a large amount is drunk in a short space of time, or if the activity following drinking is not compatible with being intoxicated. So 'short-term objectives' can refer to the safe limits set for each individual drinking session, as a way of avoiding short-term harmful consequences.

The other sort of short-term objectives are the 'milestones' that you need to set yourself, reach, and then overtake. Thus if you are gradually cutting down your drinking, you may at first drink two units fewer per day, but in week two your objectives will change to drinking three fewer units per day. You will need the encouragement of knowing that you have reached a point closer to your goal, even when you are aware that you have another month, or two months, or even a year, before you accomplish your long-term goal. Don't forget to give yourself congratulations and rewards for each objective successfully reached.

Reaching a goal is usually an uphill climb

Don't expect to get there without setbacks. Anyone who has tried in the past to go on a diet, to stop smoking, or take up more exercise, knows that it is rare to reach your goal the first time you try without hesitations and setbacks. We may start to feel 'it's just not worth it', or '*I'm* not worth it', or 'it's just too difficult'; or we get overconfident and careless ('just one more drink won't matter . . .'). You may break your rules, or you may at certain times fail to reach your short-term objectives; this should be regarded as a temporary 'lapse' or 'slip'—not as an excuse to *collapse*. A lapse may prove useful in identifying exactly what high-risk situations you will need to avoid, or find a different way of coping with in the future.

8

Targets and triggers

Planning to change something is much easier than acting on it! No-one can pretend that breaking old habits is straightforward. As we have seen, if we have become dependent on a habit we will by definition feel uncomfortable when we try to do without it. This and the next two chapters identify some of the difficulties you may face, and offer some ideas about overcoming them. On the whole, the ideas that follow are applicable whether you are aiming for abstinence or controlled drinking.

So far, you have been asked to consider four points:

(1) Monitoring the amount and pattern of your drinking by completing a drinking diary (see page 26) over a period of at least three weeks, at most three months.
(2) Weighing up the costs and benefits of the consequences of your drinking.
(3) Deciding what your eventual goal is: reduced or controlled drinking, or total abstinence.
(4) Thinking about your long-term goals, your interim goals (or 'short-term objectives') and your drinking rules or guidelines.

Getting your mind clear

Whether or not your long-term target is abstinence, if you are a heavy drinker (say, over 25 units per week, most weeks) you should have at least two alcohol-free weeks in the first place. This will ensure that, if you start a new, reduced pattern of drinking, you will do so when you are feeling physically and emotionally more in control. Most heavy drinkers who decide to have a 'teetotal' period are able to manage a fortnight without alcohol far more easily than they had anticipated. Some people may have withdrawal symptoms at first (see below), but these generally only last two or three days, and need not be unbearable. Remember that many people who have problems resulting from drinking may be only minimally dependent on alcohol, or not at all dependent, and they are unlikely to have any physical symptoms when they first stop. Those who are moderately dependent may have moderate withdrawal symptoms, that will emerge any time between twelve and 48 hours after the last drink.

In some regular heavy drinkers, the nervous system has had to adjust, over an extended period of time, to dealing with excessive alcohol intake. When these drinkers stop or reduce their drinking abruptly, withdrawal symptoms (that is, the body's state of 'readiness' for another dose of alcohol) set in. This occurs when the blood alcohol level drops and physical discomfort is experienced. It is not always easy to predict whether or not a drinker will have withdrawal symptoms at all, or how severe they will be.

Overcoming withdrawal symptoms

Very serious withdrawal symptoms including hallucinations (hearing or seeing), delirium tremens (mental disorentation, seeing things, agitation, nightmares), and fits are fairly rare. They may begin between a few hours and a few days after stopping drinking. More common symptoms are trembling ('the shakes'), nausea or retching, sweating and restlessness. The drinker may feel tense, edgy, irritable, and prone to panic attacks—and she may attribute this to 'bad nerves' instead of the physical discomfort due to withdrawal from alcohol. The symptoms tend to occur on waking in the morning or may start up to twelve hours after the last drink. Some drinkers avoid withdrawal symptoms by constantly 'topping up' with alcohol, or (particularly amongst women) by taking tranquillizers. Insomnia may also occur as a withdrawal symptom: although alcohol late at night can act as a sedative, when the blood alcohol level of the moderately or severely dependent drinker falls, she may feel restless in the early hours of the morning. Drinking is often mistakenly seen as a *cure* for insomnia, but amongst frequent heavy drinkers it may be a *cause*.

A small proportion of drinkers—those who are severely dependent, heavy drinkers—may have symptoms serious enough to require hospital treatment or close medical supervision at home, and this help with withdrawal symptoms is known as 'detoxification'. At home or in a hospital setting, you will need to be seen frequently by a nurse or doctor, your progress carefully monitored, and normally a minor tranquillizer will be prescribed for a few days, in reducing amounts. There should be no need to carry on taking medication beyond a week or so, because of the danger of substituting another drug for the alcohol.

Taking care of yourself physically in the two to five days when withdrawal symptoms could occur, or when your body is simply getting used to being alcohol-free, involves giving yourself as quiet and comfortable an environment as possible, and asking friends or family to provide you with encouragement and large doses of TLC (tender loving care). Try to arrange this at a time when you can avoid too many other commitments. Have vitamin tablets, sweet things to nibble, and plenty of interesting fruit juices available. If your appetite has been poor, it will probably improve quite rapidly; and you will notice positive changes in your memory, mood and ability to concentrate. What may take longer to establish is a regular sleeping pattern; try to be patient and concentrate on other improvements even if you have some difficulty sleeping at first.

Reducing your drinking gradually

If you have decided that you are going to reduce the amount you drink gradually over a period of weeks, you will need to plan to do it in a way that is not so gradual that you become bored with the process, but not so drastic that you find it impossible. You need to avoid a sudden drop in your blood alcohol level. If you drink in a regular daily pattern, you could aim to drink one less unit per day, and allow only one drinking 'session' per day. Or you may reduce by between three and five units per week. You will need to have kept a drinking diary for at least three or four weeks beforehand, so that you have a clear picture of what your 'reduction programme' should look like. You can either carry on reducing your drinking to complete abstinence or—what is more common—to a generally agreed 'safe limit', probably approximately fourteen units per week, depending on your personal characteristics and circumstances.

Targets

Now, after a period of abstinence, or a period of gradual reduction, you will need to pause and reflect. You may want to 'redecide' your long-term target: for example, if abstinence has brought more benefits than 'costs', or if reducing your drinking has been very difficult or not brought any benefits, you may want to consider abstinence.

On the other hand, the majority of women are moderate drinkers who rarely experience problems from their drinking. A goal of controlled drinking should enable you to join this category. You may already have worked out a set of drinking rules for yourself: check back and see if they are well-informed, realistic and reachable, and make sure they cover your particular circumstances as well as quantity. Health education literature and most experts recommend an upper limit of three to five units in any one day, combined with a weekly upper limit of fourteen units.

Identifying patterns

Look back at 'a typical week' from Janet's drinking diary, in Chapter 3. What patterns do you notice that she may need to change, in order to control her drinking?

(1) When Janet was with a group of her friends she drank large amounts.
(2) When Janet felt 'depressed and homesick' she turned to alcohol.
(3) When she drank before going on duty she felt guilty.
(4) Each time she drank more than four units, she noted that she felt bad or there was some negative consequence.

Identifying patterns can lead to setting some drinking rules to help establish control over weekly amounts of alcohol consumed. In Janet's case, after a fortnight's complete break from alcohol, she set herself the following drinking rules:

(1) 'I will always alternate a non-alcoholic drink with an alcoholic one.'
(2) 'I will never drink when I'm on my own.'
(3) 'I will never drink just because I feel homesick.'
(4) 'I will never drink within two hours of going on duty.'
(5) 'I will never drink more than six units in one day, and I will never have more than two units per hour.'
(6) 'I will keep my weekly total below fourteen units.'

Look back at your own drinking diary. Identify occasions when drinking caused you trouble, or when you drank too much. When you set out your drinking rules, bear in mind that there are many different kinds of patterns of drinking which may be 'risky':

(1) Particular people with whom you drink.
(2) Regular times of the day.
(3) When you are feeling angry or depressed.
(4) Following an argument or a relationship crisis.
(5) Drinking on more than one occasion per day.
(6) Drinking being the main focus of activity at the time (that is, not combined with having a meal, meeting friends, etc.).

Note that even if there is not much written in the 'consequences' column of your drinking diary, you could be damaging your health, or causing bad feeling amongst family, friends or colleagues, or risking an accident. 'Invisible consequennces' should be uncovered and tackled. If you are worried about your weight, or your financial situation, ensure that your drinking rules reflect a change in your calorie intake, or how much you spend on alcohol.

A controlled drinking programme should include one alcohol-free day per week, to help your body (particularly your liver) to recover itself.

By now you have probably become used to the idea that before you can change your behaviour, you have to scrutinize yourself very carefully! Everything that used to be done without much thought now has to be put under the microscope. You need to put together what you know about yourself—your actions, thoughts and feelings—and what you know about alcohol and its effects, and become what some people call a 'thinker drinker'.

'Triggers'

In earlier chapters we considered some of the broad, cultural pressures on women to drink, we have discussed possible social reasons why some women may drink heavily or become alcohol-dependent, and we have explored some of the more common psychological or emotional motives that many women (and some men) may have for 'turning to drink'. You will have listed some of your reasons and motives for drinking when you filled in your 'costs and benefits' balance sheet. We will now examine the various 'triggers' which may start an individual drinking, or continuing to drink, on any given occasion.

Your drinking diary has probably shown up specific examples of what, in the recent past, have been circumstances 'pressurizing' you to drink. These we will call 'triggers', to differentiate them from the more vague, background influences on your drinking lifestyle. These triggers are the sights, sounds, smells, feelings, people, settings and circumstances which you associate with wanting to take a drink.

Triggers are unique to each individual, and always precede actions. You need to become familiar with your particular triggers, and then start getting used to the fact that *you* can decide whether a certain action (drinking, or drinking to excess) is going to follow the trigger. It's your finger on the trigger! Looking back again at Janet's drinking diary, what triggers could have precipitated her drinking excessively? It could have been:

(1) The company of her gang (Angie, Sue, etc.) (people).
(2) Being at the social club or pub (setting).
(3) Going to a party (circumstances).
(4) Being alone and feeling depressed and homesick (feelings).

By looking at patterns of three or four weeks of drinking diaries, Janet would be able to see which of these were recurring triggers, and then set about either avoiding them, or coping with them in a different way.

List your *drinking triggers* so that you can find ways of avoiding or coping with them.

(1) With certain people? Who?
(2) In certain places? Where?
(3) At certain times? When?
(4) On certain days. Why?
(5) Linked to certain feelings? Which?

Also list your *drinking rules*.

You will be aiming to identify your drinking triggers as soon as they occur, so that you can recognize when there is a risk of your drinking 'automatically', and to anticipate certain triggers so that you can avoid them completely. If your aim is to become a controlled drinker, you need to identify and anticipate the triggers for your troublesome or uncontrolled drinking times. You will not need to concern yourself with the occasions when you drink small amounts, or when there are no problematic consequences. If you are aiming to stop drinking altogether, your target is to identify at the time, or anticipate in advance, triggers for drinking any alcohol at all.

Triggers you can try to avoid

Avoiding drinking triggers involves ensuring in advance that you don't put yourself in situations where you are tempted to drink. Some suggestions for this are: don't shop at stores which sell alcohol; or avoid the drinks section of the shop or supermarket; reduce or cut out socializing in pubs; learn to say 'no' when offered a drink; limit the amount of money you keep with you so that you can't afford to spend it on alcohol; and cut down on seeing heavy-drinking companions.

Triggers you can't avoid

You will no doubt have found that there are some drinking triggers which lead to troublesome drinking, but which you cannot realistically avoid. For instance, if your job involves serving drinks to customers, you are not going to be able to avoid the sight or smell of alcohol. Similarly, if feeling tired or irritable is a trigger for your drinking, you are unlikely to be able to avoid ever feeling tired! In these instances you will need to change your way of *thinking* about these triggers, and to learn alternative ways of responding to them.

We will first consider *external* triggers—the situations, people, times, and places that seem to be risky. If you tend to drink at home, you may find that completing a household chore is the 'cue' for pouring a drink, or starting to cook the evening meal. Your thoughts seem to turn automatically to drinking, or you experience 'craving'. If you normally drink in pubs or bars, walking past or going into one of these may trigger the desire for a drink. When you have identified common external triggers for yourself, you should think about breaking the *automatic* connection between the situation, people, time or place, and your belief 'I *need* a drink' or 'I *must* have a drink'. This thinking needs to change to 'I would normally see this as a trigger for drinking without thinking, but I now have a choice: I can make a conscious decision not to have a drink.' In other words, you are reminding yourself that you are in charge, that you are not doing something out of habit or because you 'just can't help it!'

The *internal* triggers are the mental states and the emotions that we associate with drinking—feeling tired, stressed, angry, rebellious, lonely, sad, resentful or many others. Again, we need to break the automatic connection 'I feel miserable *therefore* I need a drink' and replace it with 'I feel miserable but I don't *have* to have a drink.' With internal triggers there are two other facets that we need to bring into our thinking: (1) 'If I have a drink I may end up feeling worse', and (2) 'Having a drink won't make the reason for my feeling like this go away.'

Dealing with feelings

It seems as if one of the significant differences between men and women who drink regularly or heavily is that it is how women *feel* that most often triggers their drinking. Reading this book can't provide a way of resolving all feelings, and this chapter does not suggest that all the emotional conflicts, worries, fears, and pressures that may be linked to drinking can be recognized and disposed of in the same way that triggers such as going into a pub can be avoided. This section will simply identify some of the common 'bad feelings' and discomforts that women have found are a cue to them feeling that they need a drink.

Physical sensations

Firstly there are the feelings that are linked to physical sensations: feeling thirsty, tense, jumpy, tired, stressed, sleepless or in pain; or the nausea, shakiness or headaches that are the temporary result of stopping drinking. In the first few days and weeks of stopping or reducing your drinking, your body needs time to readjust. It may complain—you need to remind yourself to be patient. Also, you need to discover alternatives to using alcohol as a tranquillizer, a painkiller, a sleeping tablet or a sedative. Learn natural relaxation techniques or yoga (by attending a class, asking your doctor about it, or reading books), find ways of taking care of your health—for example, use the money you might have spent on drink to buy healthier foods, or vitamin supplements. Make time to pamper yourself—even if it's just one hour a week at first—doing something purely for your own enjoyment or benefit.

Premenstrual tension

Amongst some women, drinking to excess or going on a 'binge' often coincides with premenstrual tension. It may be a way of trying to escape symptoms of depression or irritability, or to deal with menstrual pains. Healthier means of dealing with these recurring difficulties need to be found (for example, taking vitamin B6, or Efamol—evening primrose oil) so that 'that time of the month' does not become an automatic cue for heavy drinking.

Sleeplessness

Sleeplessness is often an excuse for drinking, and it can be very frustrating when you continue to have difficulty sleeping when you're drinking only small amounts (or not at all). This is common too for people who stop taking tranquillizers after having been on them for a long while. Given time, you will establish a more regular sleeping pattern, particularly if you are generally developing a healthier lifestyle. Try to get a balance between physically exhausting yourself, and avoiding exercise altogether! The ideal is to find an enjoyable way of having a moderate amount of physical exertion every day, and allowing yourself enough time to wind down emotionally and physically before going to sleep. If you don't fall asleep easily, read a book, paper or magazine, have a bath, or get up and have a snack. Don't allow yourself to lie there agitated, telling yourself you *ought* to be asleep! Worries and fears can become exaggerated at night too—postpone your problem-solving until the next morning.

Worries and anxiety

Anxieties, worries, and 'how can I possibly sort this out?' are another aspect of 'feeling bad' that many women identify as triggers for drinking. There is a sense of desperation, of being overwhelmed, and not knowing where to turn. Again, the important thing is to break the connection between being faced with a problem or a worry, and taking a drink. New ways of thinking must be introduced, such as 'I will think more constructively if my mind is alcohol-free,' 'A reduction in drinking can lead to a reduction in anxiety and depression,' 'Anxiety and worry are common emotions—I'm not crazy just because I feel this way.'

In addition, you may have got out of practice, and forgotten that you *do* have the capacity to deal with difficult feelings or circumstances. But if you are seriously worried, panicking, anxious, or feel that you need help to cope, you should seek out appropriate help from an individual or an organization (see Appendix 1).

Depression

Another group of triggers for drinking are the emotions connected with feeling depressed or hopeless about ourselves and our relationships. Believing ourselves to be worthless is a cue for giving up, for escaping to the bottle. We may switch between blaming ourselves and blaming others, feeling resentful and feeling guilty, wanting to collapse and wanting to fight back. We may feel angry, frightened and confused, and a drink is the easiest, most familiar way of escaping.

Alternatives to 'bottling it up' may not come easily, because many women are discouraged from expressing negative feelings in any way—but you need to start by becoming familiar with exactly what you are feeling when thoughts of drinking are triggered. Try to separate out legitimate anger (for example, if someone lets you down) from disappointment or fear, and practise expressing your feelings directly but non-aggressively to the person concerned.

Assertiveness training

There are many examples when self-confidence and understanding your feelings will help you to sort out an emotional difficulty without resorting to having a drink. Many women find that assertiveness training courses are particularly helpful, as they are designed to develop communication skills to ensure that we come across as neither passive nor antagonistic. Many local bodies run classes in assertiveness, or one or two day workshops.

If you feel that the depression or confusion that prompts your drinking is bound up with relationship or family problems, you should seek out an appropriate person trained in dealing with these areas. This may be a minister of religion, a counsellor, a clinical psychologist, a psychotherapist, a family therapist, a marriage guidance counsellor, or a member of a group which is part of a self-help organization.

Alternatives to drinking alcohol

Easier said than done? Trying to deal with drinking 'triggers' takes a lot of practice, but happens more easily when you change what you *do* at the same time as you change how you *think*.

Have you ever thought of any 'healthy habits' or new activities you would like to try? Cutting down or stopping drinking is a good idea to introduce some of these plans.

Many substitutes for drinking are cheaper, less fattening, and healthier, for example:

(1) Try fruit juices, mineral waters, or non-alcoholic lagers or wines instead of an alcoholic drink.
(2) Instead of drinking at lunchtime or in the evening try joining a sports club or gym, going to an evening class, taking up jogging, arranging to meet up with a friend who is not a heavy drinker, doing crosswords, or quizzes.
(3) If you have time on your hands which you would normally fill by drinking, find out about voluntary work by contacting a Volunteer Bureau or a Citizen's Advice Bureau.
(4) Join a women's group or Drinkwatchers or Alcoholics Anonymous (see Chapter 9).

How to say 'no'

One of the most difficult new habits to get into at first, is refusing drinks when they are offered to you. The golden rule is to practise! Also, there is a helpful book called *How to Say No to Alcohol* which has tips and hints for those who want to limit their drinking, as well as those who want to abstain (see Appendix 2).

First, *anticipate* the situations in which you're likely to be offered a drink. *Decide* in advance what your response is going to be. *Prepare* in your mind exactly what you're going to say, and practise saying it out loud. *Be prepared* for people arguing with you, trying to persuade you. *Have an alternative* response or activity lined up.

At first it's going to seem uncomfortable—to you and those around you—but remember, once you've broken the habit (trigger: 'Would you like a drink?', response: 'Yes, please'), it will become easier and easier, and people will pressurize you less.

So, choose an excuse that you feel is acceptable for refusing a drink (such as 'No thanks, I'm on a diet/I had a couple earlier/I've decided to cut down/I'm having a bet with someone/I'm driving, etc.). State it briefly, firmly and politely—don't hesitate or waffle. When others express surprise, scepticism or try to pressurize you, don't get into an argument. Ask for a non-alcoholic drink if you want one. Smile (mysteriously!) and keep silent, or repeat what you have said. Acknowledge the reactions of those you are with (such as 'You all seem horrified!' or 'I know it's odd to hear me say no!' or 'Yes, I knew you'd be surprised'). Don't feel you have to defend yourself or justify your position, and *don't apologize*. If you are in someone else's home, ask if they have a soft drink, but if they don't ask for a glass of water. In situations where you are expected to 'bring a bottle', it is perhaps most polite to take a bottle of wine for your host/hostess and a bottle of something non-alcoholic for yourself. At a gathering where the guests' glasses are constantly 'topped up' by the host or hostess, you will need to keep a very close watch on your own glass.

Techniques for drinking less

Those readers who are aiming to cut down their drinking and keep it at a controlled level will find that their most helpful aid is a 'drinking planning diary'. Unlike the 'monitoring' drinking diary that you filled in initially to investigate your unique drinking patterns and amounts, this diary will be for recording *in advance* what your daily and/or weekly limit is going to be, and then noting the extent that you are able to keep to this. If you have an 'appointments diary', you should use this, so you can ensure that planning your drinking for the week ahead fits in with your activities. So, if for example you will be at a party with friends next Saturday night, you may allocate yourself five units (to be spread over four hours), three units when your sister and brother-in-law come to your house for lunch on Sunday, and then allow yourself two glasses of wine with dinner on three weekday evenings.

The next most important tip for decreasing the amount of alcohol you drink is to try out a range of non-alcoholic and fruit drinks, decide which ones you like, and make sure that you have them readily available. There are many brands of plain or slightly flavoured sparkling waters (such as Perrier), sparkling grape and apple juices, still fruit juices, the usual cans and bottles of colas, bitter lemon, tomato juice, ginger beers, etc. and low-alcohol or no-alcohol beers (such as Barbican), and wines (such as Eisberg), and non-alcoholic spirits. Try alternating alcoholic and non-alcoholic beverages—and make your first drink a non-alcoholic one, particularly if you are thirsty.

Other hints

(1) Drink slowly—sip, don't gulp.
(2) If you are in a group pace yourself to drink at the speed of the slowest drinker.
(3) Put your glass down between sips.
(4) Use the smallest appropriate glass for whatever you are drinking—for example, do not drink wine out of a tumbler.
(5) When drinking with a meal, have a glass of water to sip as well.
(6) Decide on specific time limits (such as 45 minutes) for each glass.
(7) Avoid cocktails.
(8) Dilute your drinks liberally (try shandies instead of beer, spritzer (wine and soda) instead of straight wine, long drinks instead of shorts).
(9) At home, get a pub measure for pouring out spirits, so you can measure 'one unit' accurately.

Make it worthwhile!

If you used to drink, say, the equivalent of two bottles of wine at home, and eight gin-and-tonics in a pub, in the course of an average week, you could in Britain be spending between £11.50 and £16.00 a week on alcohol. Reducing your intake to a 'healty' limit of, say, half that amount means that you now have £6.00 or £8.00 to spend on something else! Your 'treat' should be special just to you—of course you may want to share it with someone, but make sure it's a luxury, something that *you* want. Reward yourself as soon as you have reached your goal, and combine it with a bit of self- congratulation! Remind yourself of how determined you have been, of times when you felt very pressurized to drink but didn't, and of how you've achieved something that many people talk about but don't actually achieve.

Some people find it helpful to have a 'penalty' system as well as a reward system. Don't use penalties for not succeeding unless you also use rewards when you do succeed. One suggestion is to place a sum of money (perhaps a £5.00 note) in an envelope, addressed to a charitable organization which you don't like, at the beginning of each week. At the end of a week you must then post the envelope, if you have not kept to your drinking (or abstinence) contract; if you have kept to your contract, you can take the money out for yourself!

Rewards and penalties can be very effective in establishing control over your drinking. Do, however, bear in mind these guidelines:

(1) Keep track of your drinking patterns systematically.
(2) Decide on rewards and penalties *in advance*, and write them down.
(3) Be strict about implementing your rewards and penalties.
(4) Don't use anyone else to impose your penalties!
(5) There are no in-betweens: 'getting close to' your goal does not merit a reward. Don't bend your own rules!
(6) Chart your progress—draw up a drinking graph so that you can see at a glance how your efforts to reduce your drinking have fared week by week, and month by month.

9

Outside help

Why seek help

The word 'help' covers a whole range of activities, when it comes to drinking problems—it may involve anything from getting information about the effects of alcohol by having a quick five-minute chat to a doctor; spending a few days in hospital being detoxified; participating in a programme of group and individual therapy; or being a member of Alcoholics Anonymous. There are also many activities which may influence reducing or stopping your drinking, which you didn't anticipate as being 'helpful' but turn out to be so—for example, finding a new group of friends, a new job, a change in your family setup, or a holiday away from home.

People who have themselves had drinking problems, and so-called 'professional experts', do not all agree on what is the most effective help for alcohol problems.

As you will have gathered from this book, alcohol-related harm and alcohol dependence cover a wide spectrum from the most insignificant to the most life-threatening, and from occasional, intermittent problems through to chronic, persistent problems. There are many different theories of how problems and dependence develop, and these theories are reflected in what type of help is offered or recommended. Some organizations provide 'education', 'advice', 'coping strategies', and 'counselling', while others emphasize 'treatment' and 'rehabilitation'. The latter would refer to people as 'patients', while organizations with a non-medical approach prefer the terms 'client' or 'customer'. In other settings there is an emphasis on finding a spiritual or religious answer to the problems of alcohol abuse. If you decide to find help for your drinking problem, you will need to establish which approach you feel most comfortable with.

Reasons

The reasons why anyone decides to approach someone or somewhere to share their problems and get help for them, are many and varied. A woman may have had a vague wish and a half-recognized need for help at the back of her mind for months or even years, but she only acts on this when some kind of crisis comes up. She may, for instance, be involved in an accident or become ill. She may suddenly realize that her drinking is affecting her children in some tangible way; they may comment on her being unpredictable, or that they are embarassed by her. If she is in employment, her employer might draw attention to the way alcohol is affecting her work. These sorts of reasons may prompt her to face up to her drinking, and to start her own 'help' programme or to look for help from someone else. The important thing about actively seeking outside assistance is that she can share worries with others who know what she is talking about, discuss her fears about giving up or cutting down, air her doubts about herself and her abilities, and get guidance and encouragement in setting about changing her drinking behaviour.

Another possible reason for turning to outside help is being pressurized by another person. This may be a husband, employer, friend, or anyone close to you. It could be their actual threats that cause the pressure, or it may be that he or she is simply pushing you into doing something that you had thought of anyway. However, if you are ambivalent about exploring your drinking habits, there is a danger that you will go along with the idea of getting help at first, but then feel resentful and blame the other person, or the 'helper', if things don't go smoothly. If someone is pushing you hard to 'get treatment', try to listen and understand what their reasons are, recognize any genuine concern they have for your welfare, then take whatever decision feels honest and responsible—for yourself.

Appropriate help

Most 'help seeking' involves going to speak to someone outside your own circle of family or friends, whom you know has experience in dealing with the kinds of problems that you have. Both you and the helper should ensure that the help you get is *appropriate* to your situation. For instance, an Alcoholics Anonymous meeting will not be the right thing for you if you are trying to follow a controlled drinking programme, and a series of counselling sessions will be inappropriate if at the time you are suffering withdrawal symptoms and need a detoxification programme. Many organizations which deal with alcohol problems, as part of their job, see that they match people who approach them with the right kind of help. If a particular facility—for example, medical help—is not provided 'on the premises', efforts should be made to put you in touch with the relevant person or organization.

'Hide and seek'

No matter what reasons there are for you seeking help, it is very likely that you will have mixed feelings about it. You may feel misunderstood, despondent, under stress, or confused. You know you *ought* to see someone, but you somehow don't manage to do so. The prospect of approaching a stranger, or even 'phoning or writing a letter to ask for an initial appointment, seems to fill you with embarrassment, guilt and fear. Try to imagine what you would say to your best friend if she came to you and said 'I'm worried that I can't cut down my drinking even though I know I should, but I'm too embarrassed to talk to anyone about it.' Would you help her to overcome her embarrassment? Would you sympathize with her nervousness but still encourage her to talk to someone? Would you invite her to identify just what it is that she is scared of, and then encourage her to talk to a counsellor or other helper? If the answer is yes, try being your own best friend! Remind yourself of phrases like 'a trouble shared is a trouble halved', and 'the longest journey starts with the first step'. You may need to have some calm but firm conversations with yourself (or a best friend!) in order to make the first move towards getting help. Reassure yourself that it is understandable to have these mixed feelings, and that your motivation may easily change from one day to the next.

'Catastrophic expectations'

This phrase is a reminder that we sometimes stop ourselves from doing something new by imagining that it will have a disastrous outcome. We avoid taking risks, even if they could have very major benefits. We tend to have catastrophic expectations if we have a low opinion of ourselves, and are out of the habit of expressing our wants or needs. Thus, we hesitate to ask our boss if we can work through a lunchtime in order to leave earlier the next day, because our 'catastrophic expectation' is that she will be angry. Or, 'I don't dare ever refuse a drink when my neighbour offers, because she will think I'm a snob and will never speak to me again'; or, 'I can't possibly telephone an alcohol advice centre because . . .'

Counsellors are aware that it requires considerable courage to make the first move in asking for help. The majority of people making contact for the first time at a 'helping agency', are likely to share a number of initial fears and fantasies. For instance, you may feel guilty about 'taking up someone's time' by having an advice or counselling session all to yourself. You may feel that other people are more deserving of the counsellors' time. You may be embarrassed by some of the things that you feel you ought to tell the counsellor about. You may be worried that he or she will not understand you, or that they will be shocked by what you have to say.

To help you come to terms with some of the things that make you nervous, make a list of the most catastrophic, awful things that could happen (however improbable!) if you were to approach a particular individual or organization to talk about your drinking. Your list may include things like 'I'll be told to pull myself together', and 'They'll say there's nothing anyone can do for me.' When you have done this, make a list of the ways that you could respond if these awful things did occur. For instance, 'I would go to a different agency', and 'I would tell the counsellor as soon as I got there that I was unsure what to say.' If you take your catastrophic expectations firmly in hand, you should be able to recognize whether you are simply finding excuses not to get the help that you actually want, or whether you are having to cope with difficult but manageable feelings.

Your rights and responsibilities

Remember that as a customer, client or patient of a helping agency or a counsellor, you have the right to be treated with courtesy and respect, to have appropriate confidentiality, to have the agency's way of working and expectations of you clearly spelled out, to have your questions answered, and for you to cease contact if you are not receiving the help you need.

In your turn, you should be prepared to accept certain responsibilities when you seek treatment. Here are some of the basics: be prepared to take risks (for example, getting in touch with an agency and following it through to your future appointments!), and be honest about yourself. Whether you see your drinking as particularly excessive, or particularly low, be as accurate and truthful as you can in telling the counsellor about it. Try to be alcohol-free when you turn up for your appointment(s), or if you have had a drink beforehand, tell your counsellor. Bear in mind that ultimately choices about drinking or not drinking are yours alone, and that no counsellor or 'expert' is infallible or has all the answers.

Obstacles to getting help

In the past there has been a serious shortage of facilities for women with drinking problems; in Britain the vast majority of alcohol agencies were planned with men in mind. Psychiatrists, nurses, social workers, counsellors and general practitioners, like the general public, associated the terms 'heavy drinker', or 'problem drinker', or 'alcoholic' with males. Although men represent a larger proportion of those in any society who have drink-related problems, and are more numerous in treatment settings, the number of women needing and presenting for help with alcohol problems is growing rapidly. People are just beginning to realize that you don't have to be a homeless, middle-aged man to be dependent on alcohol—you can be any age, from any ethnic, cultural or class background, rich or poor, in employment or not, artistic or ordinary—and you can even be female!

Stereotypes

It is a long slow process for stereotypes to change, and at worst, some medical and social work professionals still treat women as if they should be passive, ignorant recipients of 'expert' advice. Assumptions are often made on the basis of minimum information, rather than the women being properly listened to. Non-specific pains and listlessness are often dismissed as psychosomatic, while depression or tension are often treated with tranquillizers. Health and social work professionals may fail to ask the right questions, so that women are not encouraged to make links between their drinking, and the difficulties they are seeking help for. This is a serious oversight because women are more likely than men to find alternative explanations for emotional, health or relationship difficulties, and to avoid identifying their drinking as the main problem. It is vital that non-specialist agencies begin to recognize that alcohol problems and alcohol dependence may well exist amongst their female patients and clients in larger numbers than they realize.

Practical problems

Some of the obstacles women face in getting help are related to practical problems such as difficulties with transport or child care for attending specialist agencies. Research shows that women with children under school age are unlikely to attend any of the alcohol agencies. This may of course be because there are few women with young children who need specialist help or counselling for alcohol problems, or it may be that they could only go if there was someone to look after the child or children. Although many alcohol helping agencies claim that they do want to attract drinkers whose problems are at an early stage, not many of them make a practical effort to encourage young women (or men, for that matter) with child care responsibilities.

Finding the right counsellor

Another obstacle is the possibility that the agency is unable to provide a counsellor or a group that the woman wanting help feels comfortable with. This will be problematic where, for example, she is struggling with issues of sexuality, or racial discrimination, related to her drinking. Many women will want to talk to someone with whom they can identify and who has been through experiences similar to their own—someone whom they believe will not have judgemental or ill-informed attitudes towards them. The accessibility of the agency, its publicity material or advertisements, the language, accents, age, and gender of the counsellors can either be offputting or welcoming to certain women drinkers.

Emotional barriers

There are many internal, emotional barriers which get in the way of women finding the help they need, and helping agencies have a responsibility to avoid reinforcing these barriers. Women need to feel safe, and to know that their difficulties will be understood and attended to. Indeed, some drinkers may confuse the barriers they themselves put up, and obstacles they feel have been placed there by others. Often unwittingly, they may blame a counsellor or an agency or a treatment unit for being discouraging or insensitive— when in fact this is a projection of their own doubts and worries. This situation needs to be tackled by both client and helper with honesty and sensitivity, in an attempt to understand what is happening (in the psychological sense).

The help-seeker needs to acknowledge that some obstacles may exist, but she must also be wary of having fixed ideas beforehand about how the helping agent will see her. It is also very important to recognise that assumptions that she will not be listened to sympathetically may be a rationalization for not seeking help. Individual counsellors' attitudes vary considerably, and the type of treatment setting will also influence how woman-orientated it is. Women drinkers represent a larger proportion of clients/patients in non-medical alcohol services than in alcohol treatment units attached to hospitals, for example, and this may perpetuate some settings being better prepared to deal with women drinkers than others. Although both men and women fear the stigma of people knowing that they have an alcohol problem, it seems that the label of being a patient in an 'alcohol clinic' or 'treatment unit for alcoholism' is one that women particularly do not wish to have. If society wants drinkers to come forward for help in resolving their alcohol problems, and it is known that there are difficulties and emotional obstacles in the way of people doing so, it is the 'treatment facilities' themselves which will have to ensure that they are providing what their clients need and want.

Family friends and work

Whether or not you tell other people that you are getting help with your drinking problem is entirely your own decision. One instance when it would obviously be appropriate for you to do so, is if you are in a job where a workmate or your boss has commented on your drinking habits. In this case, you may be entitled to time off work to attend for 'treatment'—either in a medically based unit, or in a non-statutory residential or non-residential programme, or to attend counselling sessions. If this creates difficulty, seek support from a personnel manager and/or from a union representative.

Some women have found that their family or their partner actively discourages them from seeking help. A husband, for example, may say that his wife's drinking problem isn't very serious, or that 'depression' or 'inadequacy' is her problem, not alcohol. The reasons for this undermining attitude may be related to the partner's own drinking, or his/her fear that she may 'show them up' by admitting to an alcohol problem. Once you have sought help, even if those close to you are at first supportive, remind yourself that you should not rely on other people's constant encouragement or praise, and recognize that they may not be consistently trusting of you.

Some counsellors and alcohol agencies will encourage family members to get help for themselves whether the drinker herself seeks help or not. Unless marital counselling or family therapy is being undertaken, it can be difficult if the same counsellor sees both husband and wife, or the drinker and her lover/partner. People worry about confidentiality and split loyalties. It *is* sensible and helpful for those closely involved in the drinker's life to get information or help of some kind for themselves. He or she or they should make these arrangements themselves, preferably with the full knowledge of the drinker herself. (For information about sources of help, see Appendix 1.)

Getting help

There are many different types of services available to people worried about their drinking, and it is impossible to specify exactly what you can expect from all of them. This section will describe in general terms some of the 'categories' of facilities available in England and Wales. Many other countries have similar types of organizations, though they may be fewer in number, and there may be less variety. Appendix 1 lists the names and addresses of helping agencies or contact points in England and Wales, Scotland, Northern Ireland, Eire, Australia, New Zealand and South Africa. Appendix 2 lists useful reading material.

There are some national organizations which have a central office providing information and contact telephone numbers, and/or have branches throughout the country. *Alcohol Concern* is the major coordinating body for non-statutory (voluntary) alcohol agencies in England and Wales, and it also provides information about statutory services. If you have queries about facilities in the United Kingdom, Alcohol Concern would be the best bet for you to contact in the first instance (see Appendix 1).

The organization which has branches in all the countries listed above is Alcoholics Anonymous (see Appendix 1). This is the best known of the self-help groups, and is not affiliated to any other facilities (whether statutory or non-statutory) for alcohol problems.

Advisory and counselling services dealing with alcohol problems

For many readers, an advisory, counselling, or alcohol information service for problem drinkers will be most appropriate for their purposes, or for anyone close to them (family, etc.) who wants help. The functions of these types of services include some or all of the following:

(1) Providing information about the effects and misuse of alcohol.
(2) Educating and training about alcohol problems for health and social work professionals.
(3) Coordinating resources and organizations dealing with alcohol problems.
(4) Providing information and counselling to people with drinking problems, and the families, friends or employers of such people.

They vary in size—those based in small towns or rural areas may only have two or three paid staff and will rely to a large extent on trained, non-paid sessional counsellors. They are not part of the statutory (that is local or national government-funded) social

85

services, or the national health service. You are not expected to pay for counselling, but in most agencies a donation is appropriate if you can afford it. They may use volunteers, and are accountable to executive or management committees (many of whose members are professionals). Counsellors in these agencies do not inform statutory authorities about who their clients are without first asking permission.

In the United Kingdom, many of these places used to be called 'Councils on Alcoholism' but have changed their name to Alcohol Advisory Services or something similar, and some offer a service to people with tranquillizer or other drug problems as well. You can contact them directly by telephone, letter, or personally to arrange an initial appointment for yourself, and you will normally be offered one, two or a series of counselling sessions if you wish to have them. This may extend over weeks or months, and it is important that the counselling contract is carefully negotiated and agreed upon by you and your counsellor. If you end counselling sessions but wish to recontact the agency at a later date, you can do so.

Some alcohol advisory services offer other types of help as well as 'one-to-one' counselling, for example, women-only groups, social skills groups, or family therapy. They can also recommend or refer you to residential treatment facilities, Alcoholics Anonymous, medical help, relaxation groups, etc. Opening hours are normally flexible and most services should be able to see you during the daytime or in the evening. If you want to see a woman counsellor, or have a particular need or wish, say so when you first get in contact. Anyone close to you who may wish to have counselling or information should be encouraged to contact the same agency (but a different counsellor), or another agency. If for some reason you feel uncomfortable with a particular counsellor, or using a particular service, do say so and/or try seeking help elsewhere.

Community alcohol teams (CATs) or community alcohol and drug teams

These have some functions similar to local alcohol advice services, although clients are usually referred to them by another professional—for example, a doctor or a social worker. The team members may include a community psychiatric nurse (CPN), a social worker, a psychologist and administrive staff, and have links with a psychiatrist and with hospitals which provide detoxification beds. Some teams provide a programme of home detoxification, when community nursing staff will visit and monitor clients/patients who need help during their withdrawal from alcohol, in their own home.

Day centres for problem drinkers

Mostly in the inner cities, day centres for problem drinkers are of two different types. First, there are those that provide individual counselling and groups of various kinds, where attenders are encouraged to participate in daily or weekly activities to help them tackle the difficulties of cutting down or cutting out drinking. There is the opportunity to get to know others in the same boat, and to be involved in relaxation sessions, dramatherapy, 'drinkwatchers' groups, discussion groups, etc. They are open to men and women. Second, there are day centres more appropriate to people who are homeless and need help with accommodation, welfare rights, and DHSS claims. Both types of centres are non-statutory—they may receive some local or central government funding, but the rest of their finance is from other (charitable) grants and donations.

Residential projects

These are non-medical, non-statutory projects, appropriate for people whose lives have been considerably dominated and damaged by alcohol, who see living in an alcohol-free environment as an important step in getting themselves sorted out. Many have a therapeutic programme, which includes group therapy sessions, and individual counselling. There are more for male drinkers than female, and some are mixed-sex.

Many are small, homely centres taking six to ten residents, and even larger ones try hard to avoid being institution-like. In the past, some of these projects have been stereotyped as scruffy, unattractive hostels for 'the homeless'. This is often not the case at all, and although the standard of accommodation and the help varies considerably, they have an important role for many drinkers who, following a period of detoxification, need to consolidate an 'abstinent lifestyle'. Most projects have a strict 'no alcohol' rule and residents are discharged if they drink.

In Britain, most funding for residential projects comes from the DHSS in the form of supplementary benefit payments to individual residents. Under the existing regulations (in 1988), people in employment and married women are excluded. This is one of the reasons why the large majority of residents in these projects are men—even in those for both men and women.

Some residential projects are part of organizations that also provide other services for problem drinkers; for example, the Women's Alcohol Centre in London (which in turn is part of the larger Alcohol Recovery Project) offers individual counselling and a programme of groups to non-residential clients, as well as having a house for those who need to be part of a residential project.

Private clinics

The 1980s have seen an expansion in private residential programmes for people at the more severe end of the 'problem drinking' spectrum. Most of them would expect their patients to accept the label 'alcoholic' and to understand their previous drinking lifestyle as a symptom of the disease 'alcoholism'. Treatment is closely linked to the principles and practice of Alcoholics Anonymous and abstinence is seen as the appropriate goal for all residents. Some provide help for both alcohol and other drug problems, and the staff consist of medical personnel and counsellors. Detoxification is usually provided as part of the programme, which could be anything from three weeks to six months long, and there are follow-up counselling visits and reunions. The cost of attending a private clinic is high—over £1000 a week—so the residents normally pay through private medical insurance schemes. Some projects, such as Clouds House in Wiltshire have a few places paid for by the DHSS, but there are often long waiting lists for them.

Alcohol treatment units (ATUs)

In many countries this is the main type of treatment facility provided by government-funded health services, and they are often attached to psychiatric hospitals. However, this link tends to be unpopular with the staff and patients of ATUs, and in some areas in Britian they are trying to change their image. Most have close links with nearby non-statutory agencies and ensure that there is cross-referral whenever it is appropriate. Many ATUs have small clinics in different localities, where assessment interviews and follow-up appointments can be held, and some are closing down their hospital-based premises and moving into the community.

At present, there are 30 ATUs in England and Wales, five in Northern Ireland, fifteen in Scotland, and four in Eire. On the whole ATUs are most appropriate for people who are severely dependent and/or have multiple problems arising from their drinking. Some are medically orientated and expect patients to accept an AA philosophy, and aim for abstinence. Others place less emphasis on the AA approach and—although normally recommending an initial period of abstinence—they provide help for those aiming for controlled drinking.

ATUs usually offer an in-patient or a day-patient treatment programme with a thorough initial assessment or case history, detoxification for those who need it, participation in various therapeutic groups, education about alcohol, some individual counselling, and follow-up appointments after the end of the programme. Most patients are referred by their doctor or by another helping agency, but some ATUs will accept self-referrals.

Self-help groups for people with drinking problems

Alcoholics Anonymous

Throughout the world, AA is the best known source of help for people with alcohol problems. While there are only 250 statutory and non-statutory 'alcohol agencies' in England and Wales, there are 1350 AA groups and 25 registered contact points. The primary purpose of AA members is to stay sober and help other alcoholics to achieve sobriety, and AA sees itself as 'a fellowship of men and women who share their experiences, strength and hope with each other so that they may solve their common problem and help others to recover from alcoholism'. AA groups are appropriate for people who see their drink-related problems as central to their lives, and who are conscious that they need spiritual and/or social support (from AA meetings) to overcome their alcohol dependence. There is an emphasis on accepting that alcoholism is a 'disease', and that denying that one is an 'alcoholic' is understandable, but needs to be overcome before recovery is possible.

Access to AA meetings is straightforward—look up Alcoholics Anonymous in the telephone directory for a local contact telephone number, or telephone or write to the General Service Office and you will be put in touch with an AA member. He or she will normally arrange for someone to go with you to your first AA meeting. Confidentiality is strictly honoured and only first names are used within AA. The address and telephone numbers are given in Appendix 1.

Al-Anon

This is a self-help group network (or 'fellowship') for the relatives and friends of alcoholics. Their meetings and philosophy are similar to those of AA, but people can attend Al-Anon meetings whether or not their relative/lover/partner/friend attends AA. Like AA, there is usually a very high level of sensitivity and understanding, because each group meeting consists of people who have 'been there' themselves. Al-Anon encourages 'anyone who loves an alcoholic' to give up attempts to control the drinker's behaviour or to solve his/her problem for him/her. There is support and guidance in helping each Al-Anon attender to recognize that she can only control or change her own behaviour, and that focusing on this may well reduce the stresses and frustrations of rescuing, excusing, punishing or arguing with the alcoholic.

Contact an Al-Anon member by looking up Al-Anon in a local telephone directory or contacting the Head Office to find out about local meetings. The telephone number is given in Appendix 1.

Alateen

This is similar to Al-Anon, but is specifically for teenage children of alcoholics. There are not as many branches of Alateen as of Al-Anon, but it is growing. Contacts for Alateen meetings can be obtained via Al-Anon, and telephone numbers are given in Appendix 1.

Drinkwatchers

This is a fairly recently set up self-help organization, which has scattered Drinkwatchers 'clubs' or groups in England and Wales. It is appropriate for anyone who is concerned about their drinking and wants to cut down, but who is not severely dependent. Drinkwatchers members learn techniques for avoiding and managing drinking 'triggers', socializing without drinking heavily, and preventing (or coping with) relapses. There is also a useful handbook which can act as a self-help manual whether or not you attend Drinkwatchers meetings. To find out about local Drinkwatchers groups, or to order a handbook (£2.25 per copy), see the address and telephone number in Appendix 1.

Libra

Libra is a self-help network based in Lewes in Sussex, with groups in Sussex, Kent and Somerset. It is open to anyone with a drink, drug or related life problem.

10

Risks, relapses and being realistic

Whether you decide to tackle your drinking habits by yourself or whether you get help, there are going to be times when you get stuck, or when you slide back into old patterns, and this is called 'relapse'. This happens when we try to give up smoking, or go on a diet, or with many new resolutions which have both positive and negative aspects to them. This chapter looks at some of the reasons why things go wrong, and ways of overcoming these. If you anticipate and try to understand relapse, you will be better prepared for trying to avoid it, or—if it does occur—for preventing yourself from collapsing or giving up completely.

'Good resolutions' versus 'relapse'

The fact that good intentions are not always carried through, and resolutions often don't last very long, is not unusual. Sometimes we blame circumstances, 'willpower', a personality defect, or even 'illness'. None of these is an adequate explanation. In recent years psychologists have begun to analyse the process of relapse and to try to identify ways of preventing it. There are many people who do manage to establish patterns of abstinence or moderate drinking in spite of hesitation and setbacks.

Establishing control over behaviour such as smoking or habitual drinking, it is said, is like going on a journey. The starting point is the decision to make certain positive changes in one's drinking and the destination is abstinence or controlled drinking. The journey covers some difficult territory—both familiar and strange. The traveller needs to know her own strength and weaknesses before setting off, and she will need the right equipment, including maps to warn her of steep hills, important crossroads, dangerous ditches and alternative routes. The advice of someone who has previously done the journey is likely to be helpful—particularly if she can suggest what to do if the traveller trips up, or takes a wrong turning, or meets an unexpected obstacle, or gets tired and is tempted to give up. So it is with the 'good resolution' journey: the traveller (the drinker) must have adequate knowledge of herself and of the likely route ahead. She will need to take with her skills for coping with difficult situations and clear ideas about where she is aiming for. Relapse prevention is the equivalent of ensuring that an unexpected obstacle or an error of judgement on a journey doesn't result in the traveller giving up altogether.

Risky situations

Like the traveller, the drinker who has started moving towards controlled drinking or abstinence might find that some careless decisions lead her into tricky situations. For instance, after a while, a previously heavy drinker may find that after having been abstinent for a few months she makes some new decisions that may not seem directly related to drinking, but which lead her gradually to a vulnerable position. She may, for example, agree to meet a friend at a bus stop opposite the shop where she used to buy wine, or she may agree to organize the food and drink for an office Christmas party. These seemingly harmless 'mini-decisions' can set up a chain of behaviours at the end of which relapse is almost certainly inevitable.

If you find yourself in a high-risk situation, you will either cope and stick to your limits, or hesitate. If that split-second hesitation is followed by a sense of inadequacy and helplessness, not knowing what to do, or being blocked by fear and embarrassment, there will be a tendency for you to give in. You may be unable to identify or put into practice appropriate ways of dealing with the situation without resorting to drink. In addition old thinking patterns often return at this point: for example, 'I can't handle this without a drink,' or 'I know if I just had a couple of glasses it would steady my nerves.' In a vulnerable situation, if you previously relied on drink to 'make things better', you are likely to forget your recent ability to manage without the drink, and forget all the negative consequences that alcohol previously had on you. So suddenly you are feeling inadequate and stuck, and you tell yourself that the way to get back a sense of being in control of your feelings is to have a drink.

Taking a drink or two

At this point, the odds are stacked against you, and you will probably give in to the temptation to bend the rules for yourself. You take a drink, or you break a rule of 'not more than four units' or 'not when I'm on my own'. It is not so much what or how much you drink, but the *fact* that you are breaking a self-imposed rule. This constitutes a 'lapse' or, in Alcoholics Anonymous terms, a 'slip'. How the individual makes sense of what she has done, and how she feels about it, will have an important bearing on whether or not she then has a total relapse back to her old drinking patterns.

We are probably all familiar with the 'Oh well, what the heck!' response when we've spoiled something and we feel we can't retrieve the situation. Within a very short space of time we change our view of ourselves. Before the lapse, the person may say to herself 'I'm a moderate drinker, who always carefully controls herself,' then suddenly she finds that she is acting contrary to her beliefs about herself, and this sets up a mental conflict. She will have to change these beliefs, and the label that she gives herself. She shifts to thinking something like 'Well, I'm not in control of my drinking after all—I've got no willpower . . . .' Consequently the way she acts will reinforce this; she will carry on drinking. This will also serve the purpose of reducing the guilt and anxiety she feels. The chances are that in addition to the conflict that has arisen, the drinker will blame herself for slipping up, and she will see this as a weakness and a personal failure. It means that she will probably become pessimistic about being able to stay in control when she is in a risky situation in the future.

So there is more to a 'lapse' than meets the eye. It is not just that she has a drink or two—the drinker is in danger of setting in motion thoughts and feelings that make it highly likely she will carry on drinking in an uncontrolled fashion. This makes it particularly important that we learn to anticipate high-risk situations, and find ways of reacting in a positive way to an initial lapse of commitment.

'Forewarned is forearmed'

If you are seeing a counsellor, you should discuss with him or her the situations in which you believe you may be vulnerable to relapsing. If you are working on changing your drinking by yourself, complete the relapse precipitants inventory over the page.

You will find that high-risk situations tend to fit into the following categories:

(1) Negative emotional states: feeling angry, depressed, anxious, tense, etc.
(2) Social pressure: 'everyone else is drinking', celebrations, or 'it would be impolite to refuse'.
(3) Interpersonal conflict: when you are involved in a row or difficult situation with other people.
(4) Testing personal control: when you are committed to abstinence but tempted to see if 'just one drink' really does make you want to drink more.

Knowing which types of situations are likely to be hardest for you

93

to handle means that you can focus on these and prepare better ways of coping. 'Mental rehearsal' is very useful: imagine a scene step by step and carefully plan what alternatives there are to having a drink, or to drinking more than you wish to. Practise what you are going to say if you are pressurized by others, and what you are going to say to yourself if you are fed up or caught in a row.

Keep a lookout for any apparently trivial decisions which show that you are becoming less vigilant, any ways in which you might be setting the stage for a relapse. Spend time reviewing the benefits of sticking with your original commitment, and remember as vividly as possible the unpleasant consequences that you experienced when drinking heavily.

Relapse precipitants inventory

The following are situations that you may encounter and that have been reported by people with alcohol problems as being situations which are dangerous to staying off drink. Which ones apply to you? Identifying high-risk situations beforehand reduces the likelihood of being caught off-guard.

Situation	Almost never	Sometimes	Often
1. When I pass a pub or off-licence			
2. When I'm drinking with other people who are drinking			
3. When I feel no-one really cares what happens to me			
4. When I feel tense			
5. When I have to meet people			
6. When I start thinking that just one drink would cause no harm			

continued

Situation	Almost never	Sometimes	Often
7. When I feel depressed			
8. When there are problems at work			
9. When I feel I'm being punished unjustly			
10. When I feel afraid			
11. When I'm on holiday			
12. When I feel happy with everything			
13. When I have no money to spend			
14. When I remember the good times when I was drinking			
15. When there are rows and arguments at home			
16. When I'm full of resentments			
17. When I feel irritable			
18. When I'm at a party			
19. When I start thinking I am not really hooked on alcohol			

95

continued

Situation	Almost never	Sometimes	Often
20. When I feel myself getting very angry			
21. When there are special occasions like Christmas, birthdays, etc.			
22. When I start feeling frustrated and fed up with life			
23. When I feel tired			
24. When I feel disappointed that other people are letting me down			
25. When I have already taken some drink			

(Source: Gloria Litman, 1979)

Learning from relapse

Relapse is an antidote to complacency! A relapse which does not lead to total collapse can be a very useful learning experience, and should be viewed as such. A person who has set herself an abstinence goal, particularly if she is an Alcoholics Anonymous member, may well find relapse a more traumatic experience than the controlled drinker who relapses. But for neither person does relapse constitute a failure. It highlights what you need to be on the lookout for in the future, and helps you to understand more about yourself. If you are puzzled by the reasons for your relapse, or if you are constantly struggling to avoid relapse, you should perhaps consider seeking help from an alcohol agency or counsellor.

If you have set yourself a reduced consumption or controlled drinking goal, you may find a lapse on one occasion leads you to consider giving yourself permission in advance to drink—say—five or six units at a similar event in the future. Honesty is more important than rigidity in this regard. By making an exception, and building this into your drinking rules before the situation occurs, you are being appropriately flexible about drinking limits. It is essential that you use this relaxation of limits for particular, special occasions, and that it is a rational decision which will not have harmful consequences. This type of planning is more constructive than overstrict rules which lead to almost inevitable relapse, and the accompanying resentment and guilt.

If your relapse is a small hiccup, it will be easier to face up to than if things go wrong in a big way. If you relapse in a way that affects other people, and if they begin to voice doubts about your ability to 'say when!' you may feel that you want to give up. You will probably need to choose someone you can trust to talk through your disappointment, embarrassment, fears or anger, before you set yourself some new short-term goals and start moving ahead again. Be both gentle and honest with yourself, and stick to the Alcoholics Anonymous advice to take things 'a day at a time'.

Relapse in controlled drinking—is abstinence the answer?

So far we have looked at specific relapse episodes, which could be traced to high-risk situations. However, some relapses may be caused by the drinker having chosen an inappropriate goal in the first place. The most controversial question about goals, and a difficult one for some drinkers to make a decision about, is about controlled drinking versus abstinence.

Many readers of this book will aim simply to keep their drinking at a sensible level and avoid drinking situations where the consequences could be dangerous. Bearing in mind the guidelines of previous chapters, others will try for abstinence. Some of those who set themselves an abstinence goal will follow the school of thought which argues that there are two types of drinkers: alcoholics and non-alcoholics, and that failure to control one's drinking is the hallmark of an alcoholic. Relapse is assumed to be inevitable if after a non-drinking period, an alcoholic tries to drink a small amount. It is as if she has an allergy, and alcohol can cause an immediate allergic reaction, in the form of further uncontrolled drinking. The need for total abstinence is made clear and unambiguous, and for Alcoholics Anonymous members and many other people this standpoint is very helpful in coming to terms with a drinking problem.

A different viewpoint is taken by those who argue that all alcohol drinking is a learned pattern of behaviour, and that even those who become severely dependent are not 'ill' or prone to an allergy. It is the process of learning that has gone wrong; for example, insufficient attention has been given to learning activities other than drinking, the ability to find alternative ways of relaxing, socializing, coping with anger or stress or conflict has not been developed, or the link between drinking and relief of discomfort has been too firmly established. Those who understand the problem of dependence on alcohol in these terms, regard relapse as the result of old habits not being sufficiently 'unlearned', and new ways of behaving not yet having taken hold. This does not mean that they would disagree that in practise abstinence is an appropriate goal for severely dependent and certain other drinkers. Many people find abstinence easier to achieve and more satisfying than a controlled drinking goal, and there are other reasons, such as alcohol-related physical problems, why abstinence would be recommended.

The implications of a non-disease view of 'alcoholism' are important in considering whether a relapse was a result of an inappropriate goal being chosen in the first place:

(1) There is no clearcut distinction between mildly, moderately and severely dependent drinkers, so advising severely dependent drinkers to abstain is not a very precise recommendation.

(2) Someone who is severely dependent for a short time, such as for a few months following a bereavement, may at that time appear to be drinking 'alcoholically', but it is very possible that she may return to moderate drinking.

(3) The reasons for relapse are not straightforward; for instance, it *could* mean that the drinker had chosen an inappropriate goal, or it could mean she needs more help or practice in learning to cope with pressures and drinking triggers.

(4) Relapse on one or two occasions is not 'proof' that the drinker will be unable to control her drinking in any situation in the future.

In summary, then, when relapse occurs on one, two or three occasions, it is wise to consider the points of view outlined above. If your struggle to keep to a controlled drinking goal is becoming a major preoccupation in your life, and relapse often occurs, it may be best for you to aim for abstinence.

Being realistic about goals

Much of what has been considered suggests that relapse can sometimes be 'caused' by not coping with difficult situations. We have also seen that relapse can occur because the original goal was inappropriate. There can also be problems related to the 'interim goals'. For instance, you may have decided that you wanted to cut down gradually, over two months, to a controlled drinking habit of a maximum of two units per day. If the end of your two months coincides with your annual holiday, it's quite possible you will be annoyed by your planned limits and break your own rules. Problems can also occur if your strategy for reducing your drinking doesn't suit your lifestyle; or you may decide on having one alcohol-free day between each day when you have had a drink (or a drinking session) and then you find yourself drinking more an alternate days than you did when you were drinking daily.

If your drinking has caused you difficulties because of the circumstances in which you drank, rather than the amount or frequency, you need to make sure that your goals are directly linked to resolving this. For example, if the worrying times for you are when you are alone in the house for a day or two at a time, make specific plans about not drinking alcohol at home; arrange for friends to call in or for you to go out, decide on a 'routine' which will include ways of relaxing and enjoying yourself. If your goal is simply to 'do without alcohol' you may realize that you haven't prepared enough alternatives to drinking for yourself, and the hours of not drinking may drag by resentfully and unproductively.

A strategy that can very often go wrong is one that at first glance seems the easiest: cutting down gradually over a period of a few weeks. After one or two drinks our sense of restraint is just that bit less effective, and sticking to a planned limit can at first be hard work. If on every drinking occasion you plan to drink less than you are accustomed to, you will not be giving yourself a chance to get used to a new limit, before carrying on cutting down. It is more straightforward to set clearcut guidelines, and attempt to reach your goal via one, two, or three short-term targets. For instance, during a period of her life when Pat worked as a trainee personnel manager, and her weekly drinking topped the 30–35 units mark, she decided to cut down. Her plan was to reduce her intake by one unit each time she went out for a drink. Nearly all her drinking was in pubs, with a crowd of cheerful, self-confident friends, and she found that after an hour of chatter and two pints of strong lager, she was often unable to remember whether she should be drinking six units, five units, or four units. She found that when she started to become conscious of reducing her drinking, she tended to go out less often. She began to lose track of how her levels of drinking were reducing, and she now realized that it would take at least a month for her to get down to her eventual target of no more than four drinks a day. When she did go out, she kept slipping back to drinking five or six units. Eventually—after being at home with 'flu for a week—she made a decision to change her drinking rules and intermediate goals to the following:

No more than three drinking occasions per week
No more than two hours spent in the pub
No more than four units per day

Pat achieved these goals straight away, with only a very occasional lapse.

Rewards

Drinking, as we know, seems to bring so many short-term benefits that at first it may be hard work finding alternative rewards, and recognizing the benefits of abstinence or limited drinking. When the importance of these new benefits and rewards is ignored, relapse is likely to occur. We feel sorry for ourselves, effort seems unappreciated, the whole business of cutting down seems boring, irritating and simply not worthwhile. Having a few extra drinks is the most tempting way of indulging those fed-up feelings or being rebellious. In a strange inverted justification, we can even convince ourselves that we deserve a few extra drinks as a reward for X number of weeks of not having had a few extra drinks! If this happens you need to re-examine carefully:

(1) What benefits you originally anticipated you would get from drinking in a controlled fashion, or from abstinence.
(2) What rewards you are giving yourself for sticking to your new commitments.
(3) Whether in general you are benefiting from your non-drinking or reduced-drinking lifestyle.

By confronting these questions honestly and taking the responsibility for bringing some rewards, relaxation, new interests or a change of circumstances into your life, this aspect of relapse should be overcome.

Relationships

Other people can't *cause* a drinking relapse, but our relationships with them can be a major factor in making relapses more likely.

First, in a social situation where everyone else is drinking, and where your non-drinking is being challenged, you will need the confidence and the ability to say 'no'. If you are teased, threatened, or manipulated, you might start to believe that you are spoiling things for other people by not drinking. For instance when Janet was trying to drink less, Sandy would say to her 'Oh come on Janet, you're making us all feel really uncomfortable when you sit there like a kid drinking Coke!' Try to remember that you cannot *make* people feel a particular emotion simply by drinking one kind of beverage rather than another! Both *feeling* more assertive, and *acting* more assertively, will reduce a relapse caused by pressure from other people.

Second, research shows that about a third of a group of male and female alcoholics blamed relapse episodes on interpersonal conflicts. This may have involved a conflict at work, with a friend, or at home. It could be something as trivial as a disagreement over a small decision, or a major fight or a family crisis. The tendency for many women is to blame themselves, to carry the guilt and to feel responsible for trying to make things better. Other emotions too can arise—feeling let down, cheated, angry, humiliated, lonely or confused. All of these can very easily trigger a return to uncontrolled drinking.

In addition to excessive drinking being prompted by obvious conflicts and feelings running high between people, it can also be triggered by more subtle relationship problems. For instance, your partner may undermine your achievements—perhaps without realizing that he/she is doing so. This could be because when you were drinking heavily, you relied on him/her to make all the important decisions, to take care of you if you were ill, even to scold or be angry with you after a drinking bout. This made him/her feel powerful and secure. A change in your behaviour may unsettle things, and the predictable pattern of your relationship becomes threatened. He/she may have appeared to be in favour of your initial decision to become a controlled drinker, but as times goes on he/she may encourage you to drink, and to doubt your capacity to keep to your drinking rules.

Another, more extreme example of personal relationships almost guaranteeing relapse is where a woman is constantly made to believe that she is worthless. If for instance over the years your family has undermined your confidence, criticized your ability, and attacked your drinking, a despairing helplessness may set in. It becomes almost impossible to disentangle yourself from the opinions others seem to have of you, and even the times when you are not drinking, you are full of self-doubt and confusion. Sometimes the whole family can become caught up in an atmosphere of insecurity and mistrust, no-one knowing who can rely on whom. You may need outside help to identify that this is happening, and to build up your own self-confidence. Getting the whole family involved in treatment—for instance by having family therapy sessions—is a constructive way of resolving these difficulties by enabling everyone in the family to understand what is happening.

Overcome by circumstances

Much of what has been said about relapse so far is to do with situations in which you can identify what has gone wrong, and then do your best to correct it. But life is not always like that. Thinking about your drinking may coincide with a time of taking stock of your life in general, and problems which alcohol had dulled, now return, or circumstances that you were able to ignore loom large again. You may manage to keep to your new drinking or non-drinking rules for a while, then you may find yourself hesitating, cheating, or having the odd lapse. You may find yourself faced with a painful decision—giving in and returning to the comfort and security of the bottle, or facing the difficulties around you.

The temptation to hide away from distressing circumstances is something you may feel that no-one understands. You may have experienced people's disbelief or lack of sympathy—'come on, things can't be *that* bad!' or 'why can't you just pull yourself together?'. Drinking has created a protective cocoon around you, and made things hurt less. It may also have cut you off from other people, increasing your isolation and perhaps your sense of being a victim. Only if you begin to believe that you are not totally alone in your suffering, will you be able to risk coming out of your cocoon. The first step may be to read about or meet others whose experiences have in some way been similar to your own. In Appendix 2 some books are listed in which women describe what they have been through in relation to their drinking. Meeting other women with whom you have something in common, in a confidential and supportive setting, can be done through women-only self-help groups, AA meetings, or religious organizations. This can also occur in a helping agency or 'treatment setting'. As well as, or instead of this, you will need someone to confide in—be it a 'professional helper', or some other person to whom you can speak openly. From the basis of a mutually trusting relationship, it will be possible to explore the difficulties with which you are faced and the obstacles in the way of a moderate drinking or abstinent lifestyle.

There is evidence that many women who participate in alcohol treatment programmes or groups, and in Alcoholics Anonymous meetings, have had more than their fair share of life's problems. Many painful themes may come up in group discussion or therapy sessions: having had a violent husband or father, being a victim of incest, confusion over sexuality, gynaecological problems, or grief over losing a child or husband. No-one demands that everyone talk about a particular topic, but often the knowledge that someone has been through a similar experience to you can make it easier to deal with the painful emotions that you feel.

Other issues can begin to come to the surface too: resentment over lost opportunities, worries about 'being feminine', the fears of failing to live up to other people's expectations, anger at discrimination, prejudice on the basis of class or age or race, the fear of humiliation or not having one's problems taken seriously, or anxieties about being the victim of violence and rape. Being able to share strong feelings with other women, many of them long-suppressed or little-understood, you may begin to move from the position of loneliness and isolation which contributes to drinking. Exploring your uniqueness, as well as the common bonds between women, will help you to be less of a 'victim' and more responsible for your own life choices.

11

Postscript

When someone you care about is a heavy drinker

If someone close to you is drinking in a way that worries you, you may feel drawn into the situation and feel anxious about how to cope. If you live with him or her—particularly if the drinking has been going on for a long time—you may both feel trapped in a web of confusion, intense emotions, relationship difficulties and practical problems. Even if you have the same eventual goal (a positive relationship where alcohol is not the central feature), remember that you may have very different feelings and needs which have to be attended to separately, before the common goal can be reached:

(1) You will need someone to confide in and express your loneliness, hopelessness, and worries too.
(2) You will want advice and information about how you can deal with various situations in the relationship related to drinking.
(3) Your partner may need information, counselling or medical help in order to tackle his/her drinking.
(4) It may be necessary for you and your partner (and/or perhaps the whole family) to have counselling together to resolve how each person is affected by the drinking.

Sometimes one person's needs conflict with another's: for example, the controlled drinker who has a relapse may need patient advice and understanding; his/her partner may need to express anger and disappointment. The partner's own thoughts and feelings may be contradictory and jumbled. For instance, Trudy's mother sometimes blamed Trudy herself, sometimes her husband, and sometimes decided it was she—as mother—who must take full responsibility for Trudy's drinking. She was ashamed of Trudy, but felt it would be disloyal to admit it; she was very worried about her but felt she needed to find someone who could 'get Trudy to see sense'. She felt annoyed and let down by her, but she also felt guilty about how she had brought her up. She did not know whether to treat here as a naughty child, or as a responsible adult, or as someone who was ill. What Trudy's mother needed was help for *herself*, to sort out the confusion and anxieties which in fact interfered with her being able to communicate with Trudy in any useful way.

There are many issues which you may need to tackle, including how to avoid rescuing or colluding with the drinker, and ensuring that you find a middle path in many extreme situations. You may find that you are constantly put into the role of 'victim' or 'persecutor' or 'rescuer' in relationship to the drinker. You may need to struggle with the sense that you are helplessly caught up in roles which feel uncomfortable, and you will need to reassert your own boundaries. You will have to seek out the middle ground between the view 'there's absolutely nothing I can do about it' and 'I'm sure I could stop her/him if I really tried.'

Personal responsibility

Whether we want to sort out a drinking relationship where the other person is the heavy drinker, or tackle our own drinking, we have to start by accepting personal responsibility for what we do. We need to acknowledge the circumstances of our lives and the emotions that we carry around with us, identifying the resources we can draw on, and the hurdles we have to overcome. Heavy drinking, or the problems around a drinking relationship, can lead to extremes; we may see ourselves as victims, helplessly ensnared by our family and culture or by the 'demon drink'—or we may ignore our pain and distress completely, convincing ourselves that everything is fine and no-one should be upset.

Although Janet, Pat and Trudy had very different personal circumstances and their emotional lives were very different, each of them had to face up to something within themselves, and decide what they were prepared to change. As the Alcoholics Anonymous 'serenity prayer' puts it, each person has to find 'the serenity to accept the things I cannot change, the courage to change the things I can, and the wisdom to know the difference'.

Janet

With help from a nurse tutor who was concerned about her, Janet eventually settled into her nurse training and was able to control her drinking. Apart from a few drinking binges over a three- or four-year period, she avoided using alcohol as an escape. When she left nursing and started a family, she stopped drinking altogether. In her mid-50s, however, she went through a bad patch: she felt constantly tired and depressed, her husband lost his job, and the last of the children left home. She started working night duty at a local hospital, and when she couldn't get to sleep after a night's work, she used to drink a glass of brandy.

Gradually her depression and insomnia and the amount she drank increased, and it was only when her eldest son became angry with her and insisted that she see a doctor that she shook herself out of the situation. She recognized that she should try to change her circumstances, and tackle her drinking. She found a daytime job and participated in a discussion group at a health centre. This became a support group for women discussing the menopause and health topics, and Janet was able to help herself and others, to the extent that she rapidly felt more fulfilled and stopped drinking.

Pat

In her mid-20s Pat led a busy social life. She spent her money and her time with a crowd of heavy drinking friends. She was not someone who became anxious easily, and would probably not have noticed that for two years she was drinking almost every day, and sometimes in a weekend she would get through the equivalent of three or four bottles of wine. Pat heard a radio programme one day on young people and drinking, and she decided to experiment with cutting down her own drinking. After some false starts, she found that she could reduce her drinking by quite a large amount, and she felt brighter and more energetic.

When she was 26 she met Andy and they planned to marry the following year. He was studying and they saved money by going out less often, and keeping their drinking to a minimum. Pat seldom drank more than a pint of beer two or three times a week. Thereafter her drinking was problem-free and steady, apart from two occasions when she was pregnant and barely drank at all.

Trudy

Trudy's life was for many years a rollercoaster. By her eighteenth birthday she was drinking regularly, and taking tablets, to try to cope with the mixture of feelings that seemed constantly to threaten her. She hated being alone, and if one relationship went wrong she would seek out a new boyfriend as soon as she could. She worked on and off as a fashion model and as a receptionist, but she found that she became increasingly nervous of meeting new people and she stopped working. Her father gave her money and she continued to drink more and more heavily. When she was 20, her mother persuaded her to join her for a holiday in France and while there she met and soon afterwards married a photographer who seemed to promise to rescue her from the mess she was in. She promised him she would stop drinking—and did so—but she continued to take tranquillizers and sleeping tablets. Gradually she grew more confident and happier and cut down on the pills, until two years after her marriage when she became pregnant.

Suddenly her relationship with her husband deteriorated, and he insisted that he didn't want children. After a bitter and violent few months, Trudy left him and returned to live with her mother, starting to drink heavily again after her baby was born. Every two or three weeks she would have a binge, then, full of remorse and fear, she would stop completely. For some months she attended Alcoholics Anonymous, and began to make friends. But she still felt her life was out of control and frequently relapsed—the worst time being when her father died, and she felt as if her world had come to an end. Encouraged by an AA friend, she started attending an alcohol advice agency, and through counselling she began to recognize that she would need to tackle many difficult problems in her life. She went into hospital for a period of detoxification, relapsed, went back to counselling, and stopped drinking completely for six months. She had occasional lapses after that, but learned how to avoid them becoming out of hand. She started seeing a psychotherapist and began to understand and come to terms with some of the circumstances of her life. Gradually she emerged from the self-hate and sense of defeat that had been with her for all her drinking years.

Society's responsibility

Women's problematic or excessive drinking has many different dimensions to it—the psychological (that is, the role of alcohol as a mood-altering drug), the domestic (for example, the effect of a heavy drinking mother on her children), the medical (for example, drinking leading to accidents or alcohol-related diseases), and the spiritual (for example, using alcohol to fill a sense of emptiness). And there are social dimensions—cultural (such as conventions about drunkenness being more acceptable in men than in women), economic (the production of alcoholic beverages is a powerful and wealthy industry), and political (governments affect national levels of consumption by influencing the price of drinks). The costs and benefits of drinking must be considered within all these areas, and where the situation is different for men than for women, this must be emphasized. Amongst the so-called helping professions in particular, there is a special responsibility to recognize women's position and needs.

Surveys tell us that more women than men are teetotal; in England and Wales women drink on average half as much as men do; and young women drink more than older women (9.7 units compared to five units on average per week). And yet of those women who drink over the average consumption levels, a large proportion appear to experience alcohol-related problems. And having got into difficulties in their relationships, emotionally, financially, in their jobs, socially or with medical problems, they are less likely than men to recognize that these may be linked to drinking. And they are less likely to have this possibility introduced to them by a doctor, social worker, health visitor or the like.

Male problem drinkers can more readily count on the support of long-suffering wives than a woman can rely on the support of her husband: he is likely to be indifferent or hostile towards her alcohol problem, or may even leave her because of it. If a woman needs specialist help, she will be more reticent than a man in asking for it. If she overcomes that obstacle, she will find that she is less well provided for than men, and that the stigma attached to the 'alcoholic woman' is greater.

But in contrast to all this, there *is* increasing attention being given to issues facing teenagers and young women, older women's drinking, the difficulties for women whose cultures impose taboos on drinking, or on seeking help for problems outside the family, and the concerns of those women whose drinking problems are compounded by discrimination against them on the grounds of their sexual orientation, class or colour. And there *are* changes in attitude, and gradually the need to respond more appropriately to women with drinking problems is being faced. Drinkers themselves are more aware of the role alcohol plays in their lives, and try to ensure that they stay in control of it. There is increasing acceptance of a holistic approach to health—a wish to understand and take care of mind, body and spirit. A clear example of this 'taking care of ourselves' is the ability to take responsibility for our drinking—knowing when to 'say when!'

Glossary
of terms relating to drinking problems

Antabuse   trade name for the drug disulfiram, a deterrent drug, sometimes prescribed to help people aiming to stay abstinent. If alcohol is drunk within 24 or 48 hours of taking the drug, there is a chemical reaction: flushing, palpitations, headache, nausea, vomiting and general distress occurs. Disulfiram can have unpleasant side-effects even if alcohol is not taken; but some people find these deterrent drugs very helpful. They do not affect mood or emotions

assertiveness   the ability to stand up for oneself, without being aggressive—includes, for example, being able to say 'no' when offered a drink.

assessment   usually part of the first interview or counselling session in any helping agency for drinking problems. It includes questions and discussion about your family, your drinking history, life problems linked to your drinking, your consumption patterns, what drinking does for you, and why you are seeking help. Some agencies may refer to this as 'taking a case history'

'binges' or 'bouts'   heavy drinking periods which, alternating with periods of light drinking or abstinence, form a repetitive pattern which suggests the drinker is not fully in control of her drinking habits

community-based service   a facility for drinking problems which is not in a hosptial

coping skills   ways of dealing with situations positively, without drinking; sometimes called 'self-management'

counselling   a broad term, which is sometimes used to mean advice-giving, but more accurately refers to an ongoing arrangement over weeks or months where someone with a problem or problems, in

109

some degree of distress, meets regularly with a counsellor—who aims to help her express and explore her difficulties, and find ways of dealing with or overcoming them

detoxification literally, the removing of poison; in treatment for alcohol problems this is a period of a few days when medical assistance is provided to ease withdrawal symptoms. Also referred to as 'drying out'

family therapy a psychotherapy technique which involves all or most of the members of a family, with the responsibility for a change in behaviour resting on all of them not just the individual identified as having a problem.

group therapy a method of helping people with emotional or psychological difficulties through meeting together and talking, with the guidance of a group therapist or group facilitator

liver function tests (LFTs) a blood test to discover to what extent alcohol may have interfered with the functioning of the liver

psychiatrist a medically qualified doctor who has had additional training in understanding mental illness. A consultant psychiatrist is normally head of a group of medical staff

psychoanalysis the particular technique of psychotherapy which is derived from the teachings of Sigmund Freud, and involves an in-depth exploration of the personality within an intensive, long-term therapeutic relationship

psychologist a professional trained in the science of the mind and human behaviour, specializing in applying his/her knowledge and skills in a particular setting—for example, a clinical psychologist works in the prevention, assessment and treatment of mental health problems

psychotherapy refers to various helping techniques, based on different views of human behaviour (for example, cognitive therapy, behaviour therapy, person-centred therapy) which are more in-depth than counselling and do not necessarily focus on a single, current problem. It normally involves a series of one-to-one sessions over a period of months (sometimes a year or longer) exploring and attempting to change aspects of the personality

shop-front   a term applied to some 'drop-in' facilities where information and the option of counselling is provided for people with drinking problems

Appendix 1
Who to contact for help: a selective list

Inclusion on this list does not imply recommendation.

England and Wales

Alcohol Concern	
305 Grays Inn Road, London WC1X 8QF	01 833 3471
Alcohol Concern (Wales)	
c/o Heartbeat, 24 Park Place, Cardiff CF1 3BA	0222 378855
Alcoholics Anonymous	01 352 9779/5493
PO Box 514, 11 Redcliffe Gardens,	
London SW10 9BQ	York (0904) 644026
Al-Anon family groups	01 403 0888
Alateen	01 403 0888
Drinkwatchers	
c/o ACCEPT, 200 Seagrave Road,	
London SW16 1RQ	01 381 3857

London

DAWN London (Drugs Alcohol Women Nationally)	01 700 4653
Women's Alcohol Centre	01 226 4581
GLAAS (Greater London Alc. Advisory Serv.)	01 253 6221/2
ACCEPT (Addictions Community Centres for Education, Prevention, Treatment and Research)	01 381 3155
ACS (Alcohol Counselling Service)	01 737 3579
ARP (Alcohol Recovery Project)	01 403 3369
AA (London Region Telephone Service)	01 352 3001

Many boroughs have their own alcohol counselling/advice services, and some have specific services for lesbian women, for disabled women and/or women from ethnic minority communities. Contact DAWN or GLAAS or ARP or ACS for this information. Information about residential treatment in London can be obtained from Alcohol Concern.

There are councils on alcohol, or advice and counselling services, in most big cities and towns, often acting as a referral point for facilities throughout a county. They are usually listed in telephone directories under 'Alcohol advice . . .' or 'Alcohol counselling . . .', or prefixed with the name of the county. They may also come under an 'addiction' heading, such as 'Kent Council on Addiction'. Alternatively, write to or telephone Alcohol Concern, London or Wales.

Scotland

Scottish Council on Alcohol   041 333 9677
  137–145 Sauchiehall Street, Glasgow G2 3EW

There are councils on alcohol and advice centres in many areas and districts (only some are listed here). Contact the SCA.

Aberdeen	0224 573887
Ayrshire	Kilmarnock 41155
Borders	
96 High Street, Galashiels	
Central	Stirling 63031
Dumbarton	West Bridgend 31456
Edinburgh	031 225 8888
Fife	Glenrothes 759543
Glasgow	(041) 333 9111
Inverclyde	Greenock 85695
Inverness	0463 220995
Orkney	Kirkwall 4738
Renfrew	041 887 0880/889 1061
Tayside	Dundee 23965

Eire

Many hospitals have in-patient and out-patient facilities for problem drinkers, but there are very few community-based services. For information about local facilities, contact:

Irish National Council on Alcohol
  19–20 Fleet Street, Dublin 2   0001 774832

Alcoholics Anonymous   0001 774809

Northern Ireland

Northern Ireland Council on Alcoholism sees clients from all parts of Ireland and runs a women-only group. There are satellite centres outside of Belfast. They also provide information about NHS and private facilities.

Northern Ireland Council on Alcoholism
40 Elmwood Avenue, Belfast BT9 6AZ   0232 664434

South Africa

The South African National Council on Alcoholism and Drug Dependence (SANCA) provides information and motivational services for all population groups. The Head Office is:
P.O. Box 10134, Braamfontein 2001   011 725 5810
    If you have difficulty in finding an alcohol service in your area, contact a local AA branch (see telephone directory) or write to SANCA Head Office.

AA (Western Cape)	021 24 7559
Alanon (Western Cape)	021 23 3411

Some local offices of SANCA

Cape Town	021 245260
400 Namaqua House, 36 Burg Street	
Atlantis	0226 469243
Bloemfontein	051 84607
	051 477271
Durban	031 304 9631
Nazaret	(Middleburg) 5331
East London	0431 21257
Pietersburg	01521 3700
Johannesburg	011 836 5942
Soweto (Moroka)	011 986 1109
	011 673 6105
Kimberley	0531 26172

New Zealand

The treatment of alcohol problems is supported in New Zealand by the Alcoholic Liquor Advisory Council who publish the *Directory of Addiction Services in New Zealand*; copies of this can be obtained from
PO Box 5023, Wellington   04 720997
    There are alcohol and drug centres or alcohol clinics in most towns and cities, and some are listed below:

Auckland Community Alcohol Services   09 860808

Hamilton Community Alcohol Services	071 394352
New Plymouth Taranaki Base Hospital	067 36139
Napier Addiction Services	070 54496
Wellington Alcohol and Drug Centre	04 898340
Nelson Alcohol Clinic	054 88299
Dunedin Centre for Alcohol-related Disabilities	024 772323
Christchurch Alcohol and Drug Centre	03 50983
The Vine (Women only)	03 553930
Rawene (Northland) Lesbian Haven	Rawene 819

There are also 'field offices' of the National Society on Alcoholism and Drug Dependence in many towns, where assessment and referral interviews take place. Contact telephone numbers can be found in local telephone directories.

Alcoholics Anonymous and Al-Anon groups are found throughout New Zealand. Telephone numbers can be obtained through Alcohol Treatment Centres or Citizens' Advice Bureaux. The AA Central Office is:

P.O. Box 6458, 1st Floor, 72–74 Taranaki Street, Wellington

04 859 455

Australia

An Australian *Directory of Services* for alcoholism and drug dependence is available from the Marketing Division, Alcohol & Drug Foundation Australia, PO Box 269, Woden, A.C.T. 2606.

Alcohol and Drug Foundation Australia is a national coordinating body which provides information about what treatment services are available throughout the country:

ADFA
19–23 Townshend Street
Phillip
ACT 2606

There are also Alcohol and Drug Foundations in the following cities and towns which provide information about services in their territory or state:

Canberra	062 474747 *or* 472853
Waterloo	02 6634255 *or* 02 6634256
Spring Hill	07 8323798
Aitkenvale	077 799011 *or* 715181
Adelaide	08 231 0822
Moonah	002 288256
Melbourne	03 690 6000

Alcoholics Anoymous groups and Al-Anon Family Groups (and Alateen) exist in several hundred cities and towns. Main offices are in the following:

Sydney	AA: 02 799 1705/1724
	Alanon: 02 264 9255
Melbourne	AA: 03 429 1833
	Alanon: 03 63 3368
Brisbane	AA: 07 832 3141
	Alanon: 07 229 2501
Adelaide	AA: 08 42 2977/5537
	Alanon: 08 51 2959
Canberra	AA: 062 491340
	Alanon: 062 48 8651
Perth	AA: 09 325 3209
	Alanon: 092 325 7528
Hobart	AA: 002 348711
	Alanon: 022 23 4244
Darwin	AA: 089 854479

Community health centres are a good first contact or referral point for people with alcohol problems, and are located in most cities and towns throughout Australia. Call the nearest Health Department office, or Telecom Directory Assistance, to contact your nearest centre.

Lifeline is a 24 hour telephone counselling service for crisis situations. For local telephone numbers contact the 'Help' pages of your telephone directory.

Projects for women with alcohol (or other drug) problems:

Guthrie House in Enmore, NSW	02 516 5588
Jarrah House in Canterbury, NSW	02 789 4311
Women's Health Centre in Coff's Harbour, NSW	043 921341

Appendix 2
Recommended reading

If you find reading to be a helpful way of sorting out difficulties in your life, here is a list of books about alcohol problems and excessive drinking that are worthwhile getting hold of (and are inexpensive).

'Self-help manuals' for cutting down drinking

There are none that are for women only, and they tend to be written either for British or American readers. But they can be useful, particularly if you're 'going it alone'.

Accept Services UK *Drinkwatchers' Handbook*, ACCEPT Services UK, 200 Seagrave Road, London, SW6 1RQ (01 381 3155) £2.25

Grant, M. (1984) *Same Again – A Guide to Safer Drinking*, Penguin Books, Harmondsworth

Gwinner, P. and Grant, M. (1979) *What's Your Poison?*, BBC Publications

McNeill, K. (1986) *How to Say No to Alcohol*, Sheldon Press, London

Miller, W. R. and Munoz, R. F. (1987) *How to Control Your Drinking*, Sheldon Press, London

Robertson, I. and Heather, N. *Let's Drink to Your Health!* Produced by the British Psychological Society Distribution Centre, Black Horse Road, Letchworth, Herts SG6 1HN

Scottish Health Education Group *So You Want to Cut Down Your Drinking?*, Scottish Health Education Group, Woodburn House, Canaan Lane, Edinburgh EH10 4SG

Books about drinking and drinking problems

For women drinkers

McConville, B. (1983) *Women Under the Influence: Alcohol and its Impact*, Virago Press, London

Sandmaier, M. (1980) *The Invisible Alcoholics*, McGraw-Hill, New York

Wolfson, D. and Murray, J. (eds) (1986) *Women and Dependency*, DAWN (London) (contact via Omnibus Workspace, 39–41 North Road, London N7 9DP)

About women drinkers

Bauer, J. (1982) *Alcoholism and Women—The Background and the Psychology*, Inner City Books, Toronto

Breeze, E. (1985) *Women and Drinking – An enquiry carried out on behalf of the DHSS*, Her Majesty's Stationery Office, London

Camberwell Council on Alcoholism (1980) *Women and Alcohol* Tavistock, London and New York

Plant, M. (1985) *Women, Drinking and Pregnancy*, Tavistock, London

Wilsnack, S. C. and Beckman, L. J. (eds) (1984) *Alcohol Problems in Women*, Guildford Press, New York

General interest

Edwards, G. (1982) *The Treatment of Drinking Problems—A Guide for the Helping Professions*, Blackwell Scientific Publications Limited, Oxford

Robinson, J. (1988) *On the Demon Drink*, Mitchell Beazley, London

Royal College of Physicians (1987) *A Great and Growing Evil—The Medical Consequences of Alcohol Abuse*, Tavistock, London and New York

Royal College of Psychiatrists (1986) *Alcohol—Our Favourite Drug*, Tavistock, London and New York

Emphasis on the family

Burr, A. (1982) *Families and Alcoholics*, Constable and Company Limited, London

Burton, M. (1974) *An Alcoholic in the Family*, Faber and Faber, London

Meyer, M. L. (1982) *Drinking Problems—Family Problems*, Momenta Press,

Books on subjects relevant to women's alcohol problems

Dickson, A. (1982) *A Woman in Your Own Right*, Quartet Books, London

Haddon, C. (1984) *Women and Tranquillizers*, Sheldon Press, London

Nairne, K. and Smith, G. (1983) *Dealing with Depression*, The Women's Press

Sanders, D. (1984) *Women and Depression—A Practical Self-help Guide*, Sheldon Press, London